LABORUM DULCE LENIMEN

G. SCHIRMER

# TOSCA

OPERA IN THREE ACTS

(After the play by Victorien Sardou)

Libretto by

GIUSEPPE GIACOSA and LUIGI ILLICA

ENGLISH VERSION BY JOHN GUTMAN

MUSIC BY

## GIACOMO PUCCINI



VOCAL SCORE

Ed. 2235

G. SCHIRMER

New York

## Note

## CAST OF CHARACTERS

FLORIA TOSCA, an opera singer . . . . . . . . . . . . . *SOPRANO*

MARIO CAVARADOSSI, a painter . . . . . . . . . . . . . *TENOR*

BARON SCARPIA, the chief of the Roman police . . . . . . *BARITONE*

CESARE ANGELOTTI, an underground fighter . . . . . . . . . *BASS*

A SACRISTAN . . . . . . . . . . . . . . . . . . . . . . *BARITONE*

SPOLETTA, a police agent . . . . . . . . . . . . . . . . *TENOR*

SCIARRONE, Baron Scarpia's orderly . . . . . . . . . . . . . *BASS*

A JAILER . . . . . . . . . . . . . . . . . . . . . . . . . *BASS*

A SHEPHERD BOY . . . . . . . . . . . . . . . . . . . *SOPRANO*

A Cardinal; A Judge;
Roberti, Executioner; A Scribe;
An Officer; A Sergeant;
Soldiers; Police-Agents; Ladies; Nobles; Citizens.

Rome — June 1800

## CONTENTS

# TOSCA

Libretto by
Giuseppe Giacosa and Luigi Illica
After the play by Victorien Sardou
English Version by
John Gutman

Giacomo Puccini

## ACT I

### THE CHURCH OF SANT' ANDREA DELLA VALLE

(At the right, the Attavanti Chapel. A dais on the left: on it, a large picture on an easel covered by a piece of cloth. Painter's tools lie about, also a basket.)

Vivacissimo con violenza ♩ = 168
ff (The curtain rises.)
1
p dim.
(Angelotti enters looking like a prisoner, emaciated, exhausted, trembling with fear, breathing heavily.)
rall.
(Surveying the scene with a rapid glance.)
più rall. e dim:
sostenendo
pp

QUASI LENTO
ANGELOTTI
a piacere
Ah!... Final_men_te!... Nel terror mio stolto vedea
Ah! I can breathe now... Ter- ri- fy- ing fac- es every-
QUASI LENTO
col canto

(He gives a start — then takes a careful look as though reconnoitering the scene.)

VIVACE COME PRIMA
A.
cef_fi di birro in o_gni vol_to.
— where in the most un- like- ly pla- ces!
VIVACE COME PRIMA
2
f
ff
p

(Seeing the pillar with the holy water basin and the Madonna, he heaves a sigh of relief.)

a piacere
A.
La pi_la... la co_
The ba- sin and the
col canto

*a tempo*

A -lonna... «A
pil- lar... and

*a tempo*

*p*

3

(Going closer to the pillar.)

*rall.* *a tempo*

A. piè della Ma_don_na» mi scrisse mia so_rel_la...
this is the Ma- don- na my sis- ter said to look for.

*rall. col canto*..........................

*p a tempo*

(Angelotti looks for the key at the foot of the Madonna.)

*p dolce*

*p*

(Not finding it, he goes on searching in great excitement.)

3 3

*rall:*...................................... *f*

4
(With a gesture of discouragement.)
p a tempo
f
3

ben cantando
(Starts looking for the key again.)
pp
cres.
3

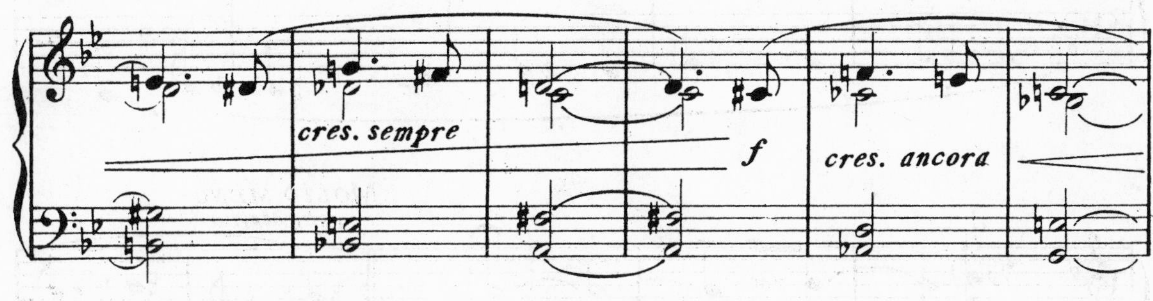
cres. sempre
f
cres. ancora

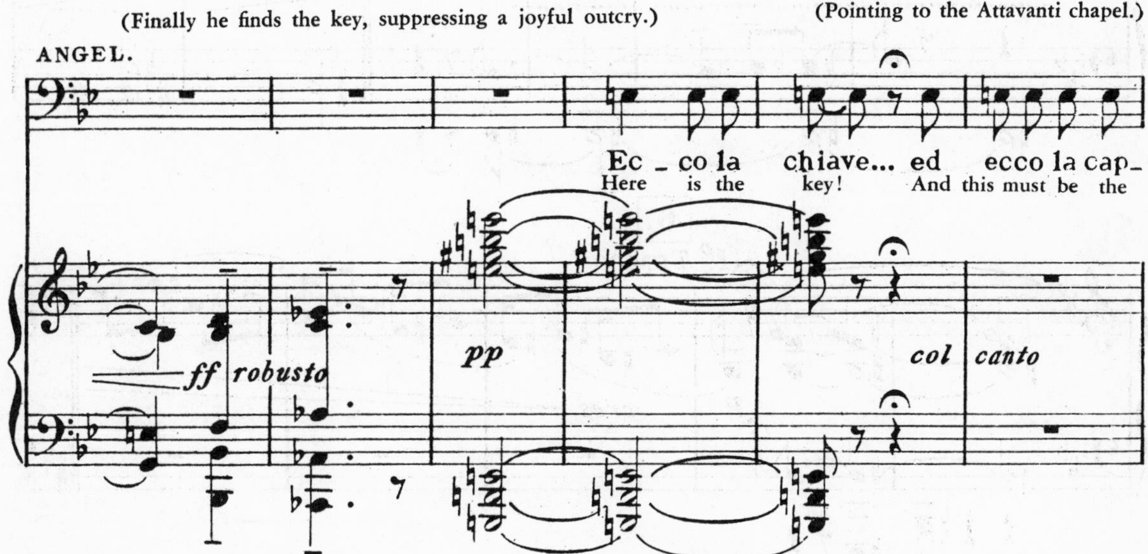
(Finally he finds the key, suppressing a joyful outcry.)
(Pointing to the Attavanti chapel.)
ANGEL.
Ec _ co la chiave... ed ecco la cap_
Here is the key! And this must be the
ff robusto
pp
col canto

a tempo
(Frightened again to be discovered, he glances around, then walks over to the chapel,
A.
- pella!..
chap-el.
5
ff a tempo
p
p
very cautiously inserts the key, opens the gate and disappears after having locked the gate again.)
rall:
Molto meno
espressivo
6
I.º Tempo
p
cres.
3

(The Sacristan appears at the back; moving from right to left he begins to attend to his chores;

*All.tto grazioso* ♩ = 132

*p*

he carries a bunch of paint brushes.)

*legato*

*p*

7

*f*

*p*

*f*

*p*

8
p
scherzoso
2
2
p
9
p
tr
(The Sacristan walks up to the dais, speaking aloud, as though talking to somebody.)
10
p

(He has a nervous tic: a quick twitch of the neck and the shoulders.)

IL SAGRESTANO

E sem_pre la _ va!..
I clean his brush - es,

SAGR.

Ogni pennel_lo è soz _ zo peggio d'un col_la_rin d'u _
That is my fav - 'rite pas - time! Yet they are al - ways fil - thier

*legato*

*p*

SAGR.

_no sca _ gnoz _ zo... Signor pit_
than the last time. Sig- nor, good

(Looking at the dais, he is surprised at finding it empty.)

SAGR.

_to _ re... **11** Tò!.. Nessuno.
morn - ing! What? No paint-er?

*f*

*p*

SAGR.
Avrei giu_ra_to che fos_se ri_tor-
And I was cer-tain that I had heard his
cres.
f
p
(He puts down his paint brushes and climbs on the dais.)
SAGR.
_na_to il ca_va_lier Cava_ra_dossi.
foot-steps, my no-ble friend, Cava-ra-dos-si.
cres.
p
Ritenuto
12
A Tempo
(Peers into the basket.)
f
p
SAGR.
(Comes down from the dais.)
No, sbaglio. Il paniere è intat_to.
No, cu-rious. No one touched the bas-ket.
p
p

(The Angelus is being rung. The Sacristan kneels down and prays humbly.)

a tempo
SAGR.
Et Verbum ca_ro factum est _et ha_bi_ta_vit in
a tempo

CAVARADOSSI (Cavaradossi comes in through the side door; he sees the Sacristan kneeling.)

Che fai?
What's this?
(Getting up.)
rall.
SAGR.
no_bis...
Re_ci_to l'An_gelus.
Say- ing an An- ge- lus.
rall:
pp

14

(Cavaradossi steps on the dais and uncovers the picture: a painting of Mary Magdalen with big blue-

ANDte MODto
p

eyes and golden hair to her shoulders. He gazes at the picture with silent attention.)

cres.
p cres.
accelerando
(The Sacristan is about to speak to Cavaradossi; he sees the painting and exclaims in great astonishment.)
SAGR.
Sante ampolle!
Good-ness gra-cious!
15
ff
p
fp
(Addressing the Sacristan.)
CAVAR.
UN POCO PIU
Di chi?
You do?
SAGR.
Il suo ritratto!..
I know that la- dy.
UN POCO PIÙ
Di quell'i_gno_ta
That-love-ly—stran-ger.
pp

SAGR.

chei dì pas _ sa _ ti a pre _ gar qui ve _
The _ past few morn _ ings she's _ come _ here to

(Pointing to the statue of the Madonna

SAGR.

_ nì _ _ _ a tut _ ta de _
wor _ _ _ ship with great de _

CAVAR.

(Smiling.)

where Angelotti had found the key.)

È ve _ ro.
I've seen her.

SAGR.

_ vo _ ta e pi _ _ _ a...
_ vo _ tion _ and _ feel _ _ ing.

16

*p*

CAV.

E tan _ to el _ l'e _ ra infer _ vo _ ra _ _ ta
She was so lost to all a _ round her

*p*

CAV.
nel - la sua pre - ghie - ra
that she nev - er saw me
ch'io ne
all the
CAV.
pin - si, non vi - sto,
time I was paint - ing
il bel sem - bian -
her love - ly fea -
m.s.
CAV.
te.
- tures.
(Shocked.)
SAGR.
(Fuo - - - ri,
Sa - - - tan,
Sa - ta - na, fuo - ri!)
get thee be - hind me!
f
mf
p
pp
(To the Sacristan, who does as he is told.)
rall.
CAV.
Dammi i co -
Give me my
rall.

AND.te LENTO ♩= 48
(Cavaradossi starts to paint, interrupts himself often to scrutinize his
CAV.
- lo - ri!
brush - es.
17
AND. LENTO ♩= 48
p
3
3
p

own work, while the Sacristan, sitting at the foot of the dais, begins his work.)
pp

(Cavaradossi again interrupts his painting: takes out of his
3
3
pp

pocket a medallion, and his eyes begin to wander from the miniature in the medallion to the painting.)
CAVAR.
Re -
In
18
pp

PIÙ LENTO
CAV.
pp
con-di-ta ar-mo-ni - a di bel-lez-ze di-
strange mys-te- rious fash- ion beau-ty's face is e-
PIÙ LENTO
dolciss.
pp
Sostenendo
pp
ver - se!... È bru - na Flo - ri - a, l'ar-
ter - nal. My To - sca burns with love, a-
Sostenendo
sf
rall:.................. a tempo
p
dente aman-te mi - a, e
glow with flam-ing pas - sion. My
(Mumbling to himself.)
(He goes to find some water for his work.)
SAGR.
pp
(Scherza coi fanti e lascia stare i san - ti...
Once she's been painted they will get ac-quaint - ed.
pp rall:.................. a tempo
m.d.
p

CAV.
te, - bel - ta - - de i - gno - ta,
love - ly stran - - ger is mild as spring,
pp
CAV.
cin - ta di chio - me bion - - de!...
gold - en curls on her shoul - - der,
CAV.
Tu az - zur - ro hai l'oc - chio
eyes as blue as heav - en;
CAV.
To - sca ha l'oc - chio ne - ro!
dark as night are To - sca's.
SAGR.
(He returns and says, with indignation.)
Scherza coi fanti e lascia stare i
Once she's been painted they will get ac-
p

Lo stesso mov.to
CAV.
L'ar_te nel suo mi - ste - ro le di-
Art, with a spell of mag - ic, makes the
(He starts cleaning the brushes again.)
SAGR.
san_ti!
- quaint-ed.
Lo stesso mov.to
19
p
CAV.
rall:
- ver-se bel_lez_ze in-siem con - fon - de: ma
two seem like one to the be - hold - er. My
col canto
I.o Tempo
CAV.
nel ri - trar co - ste - - i....
art knows man - y fac - es,
SAGR.
opp.
Que_ste di_ver_se gon - ne
It's this one or an - oth - er,
I.o Tempo
p

CAV.
il mio so - lo pen - sie - ro,
but my heart nev - er chang - es:
SAGR.
che fanno concor - ren - za al - le Ma - don - ne mandan
they all presume to ri - val the Ho - ly Moth - er. What a
allarg.
rit.
ah! il mio sol pen - sier sei tu! To - sca sei
have vowed my love to you, To - sca, to
tan - fo d'infer - no.
stench of dam-na - tion!
allarg. col canto
(Continues his painting.)
tu!
you! (Dries the brushes and goes on mumbling.)
Scherza coi fanti e la - scia stare i san - ti.
Once she's been painted they will get ac - quainted ed.
dolciss.
ppp

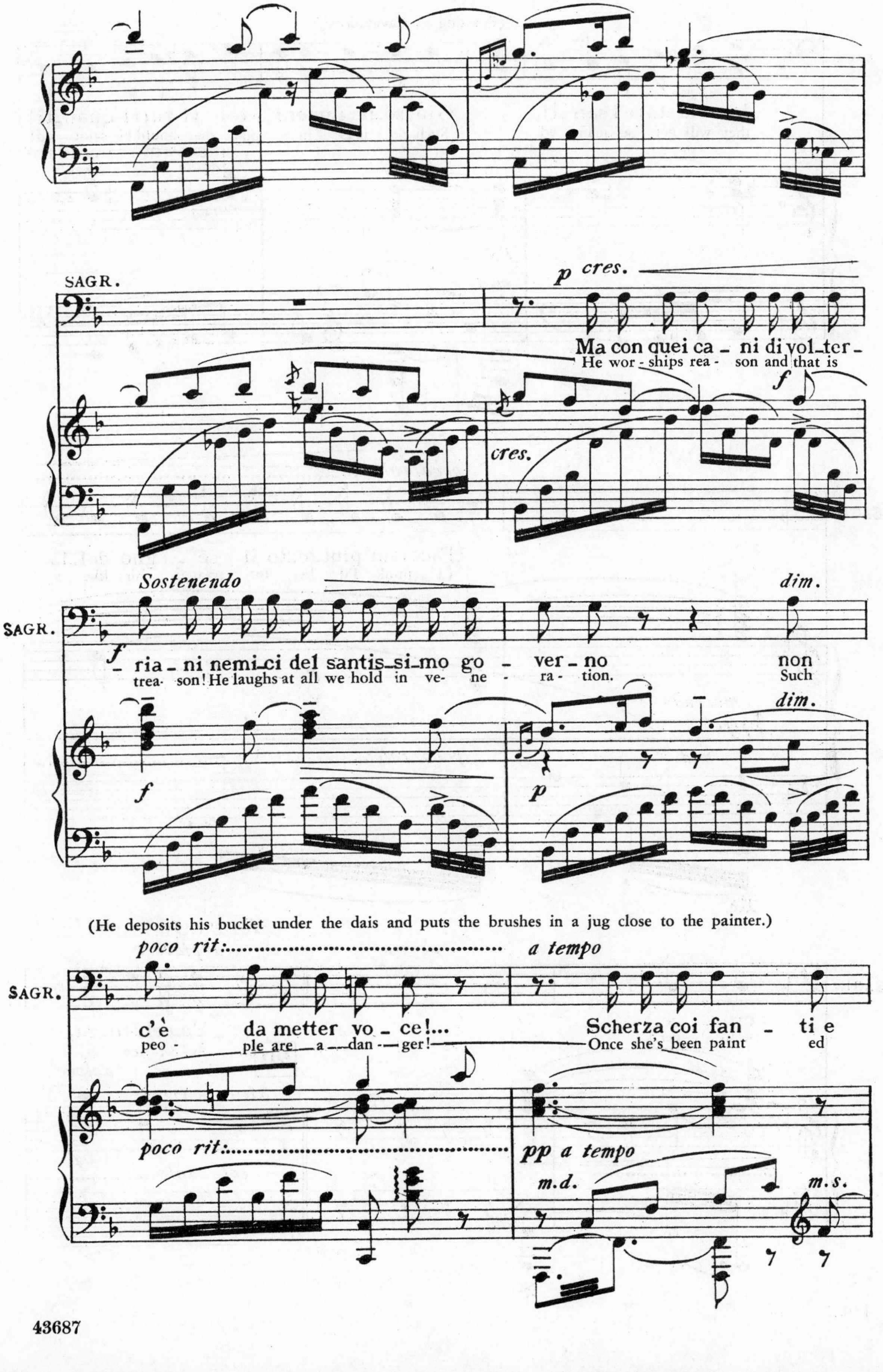

SAGR.

*p cres.*

Ma con quei ca - ni di vol - ter -
He wor - ships rea - son and that is

*cres.* *f*

*Sostenendo* *dim.*

SAGR.

*f* - ria - ni nemi - ci del santis - si - mo go - ver - no non
trea - son! He laughs at all we hold in ve - ne - ra - tion. Such

*dim.*

*f* *p*

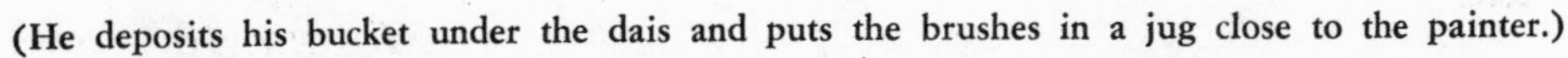
(He deposits his bucket under the dais and puts the brushes in a jug close to the painter.)

(Pointing at Cavaradossi.)
SAGR.
la_scia stare i san_ti,
they will get ac-quaint-ed.
Già, so_no impeni - ten_ti tutti quan_ti!
Such do- ings in a place that should be saint- ed!
pp
m.d.
m.s.
poco rall:
SAGR.
(Facciam piut_tosto il se - gno del_la
(I think I'd bet- ter treat him like a
morendo
ppp
m.d.
poco rall:
Ped.
MODERATO
a piacere
SAGR.
cro - ce.)
stran - ger.)
Ec_cel_len_za,
Ex- cel- len- cy,
20
MODERATO
col canto

(Continues painting.)
CAVAR.
ALL.^tto I.^o TEMPO
Fa il tuo pia - ce - re!...
I do not need you.
SAGR.
va - do.
may I?
Pieno è il pa - nie - re... Fa peni - ten - za?
Here is your bas - ket. Aren't you eat - ing?
p
CAV.
Fa - me non ho.
No, I won't eat.
(He rubs his hands ironically; cannot suppress
Oh!... mi rin - cre - sce!...
No? I am sor - ry.
a tempo
spigliato
col canto
a joyful gesture and a greedy look at the basket, which he puts aside carefully.)
(Taking a pinch of snuff.)

CAVAR.
(Busy painting.)
Va!...
Go!
SAGR.
Badi, quand'e_sce chiu _ da.
Do not for- get to lock up.
(Leaving.)
SAGR.
Vo!
Good.
(Cavaradossi paints, turning his back to the chapel. Angelotti, assuming the church to be empty, appears
legato
pp
dim.
rall. molto
behind the gate and is about to open it.)
(Cavaradossi, hearing the key in the lock, turns around.)
CAVAR.
21
Gen_te là
What can that
pp

(Angelotti, terrified by Cavaradossi's move, stops and wonders if he had better hide in the chapel again, but looking up he finds it hard not to cry out with joy: he has recognized Cavaradossi and stretches his arms towards him, delighted to find unexpected help.)

ALL.º MOLTO AGITATO
CAV.
dentro!...
noise be?
ALL.º MOLTO AGITATO
ff
ANGELOTTI
Voi!
You!
Ca - va - ra -
Ca - va - ra -
ff marcatissimo
(Cavaradossi does not recognize him and remains on his dais in amazement.)
A.
- dos - - si!
- dos - si!
Vi man - da Id - di - o!
God must have sent you!
p
(Angelotti steps up to him so that he would recognize him.)

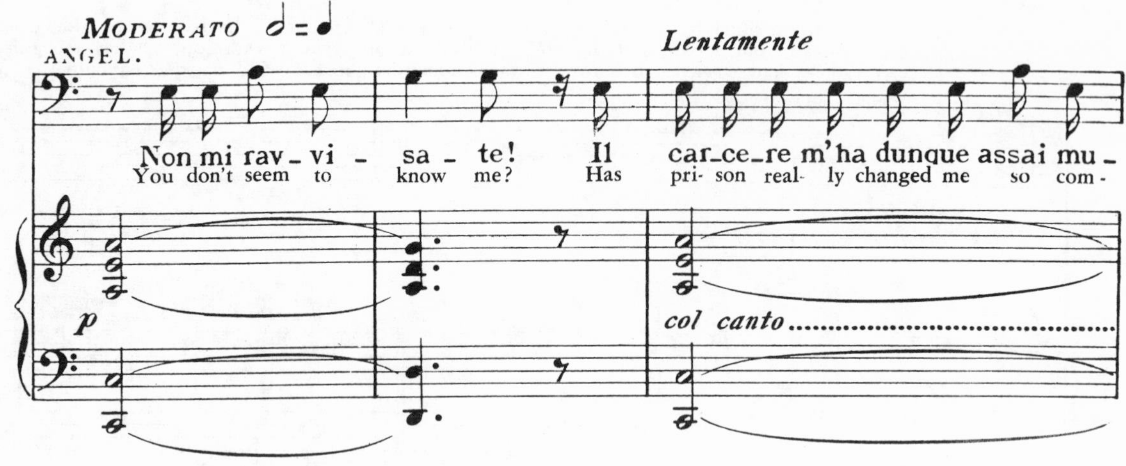
Moderato
Lentamente
ANGEL.
Non mi rav_vi - sa _ te! Il car_ce_re m'ha dunque assai mu_
You don't seem to know me? Has pri- son real- ly changed me so com-
p
col canto

(Cavaradossi, recognizing him, quickly puts down his palette and brush and comes down from the dais towards Angelotti.)

CAVAR.
con slancio
An - ge - lot - - ti! Il
An - ge - lot - ti! The
A.
_ta _ to!
_plete - ly?
string.

rapidamente, declamato, con forza
(He hastily locks the side entrance.)
All.° vivo e agitato
CAV.
Con_so_le del_la spenta repubbli_ca ro _ mana.
gov- er- nor of the o-ver-thrown Ro-man Re - public.
22
col canto
ff

(Walking up to Cavaradossi.)
(In a whisper.)
ANGEL.
Fug-gii pur o-ra da Ca-stel San-
I have es-caped at last from Fort Sant'
mf
CAVAR. (Magnanimously.)
Di-spo-ne-te di me.
Tell me what I can do!
A.
-t'An-ge-lo...
An-ge-lo.
TOSCA (Outside the church door.)
Ma-rio!
Ma-rio!
(Hearing Tosca's voice, Cavaradossi motions to Angelotti to be silent.)
CAV.
Ce-la-te-vi!
Go hide yourself.
pp
p

CAV.
p
È u-na don-na...ge-lo-sa.
I don't want her to see you.
mf
TOSCA
Ma-
Ma-
CAV.
Un bre-ve i-stante e la ri-man-do.
I will be with you in a mo-ment.
p
pp
T.
-rio!
-rio!
(Speaking towards the door from where Tosca's voice is heard.)
CAV.
Ec-co-mi!
Here I am.

23
(Angelotti, growing faint, leans against the dais and moans.)
(Cavaradossi quickly grasps the basket and hands it to Angelotti.)
ANGEL.
So_no stre_mo di for_ze, più non reggo...
I can't stand it much longer, I'm ex- haus-ted...
24
CAVAR.
In que - sto pa - nier v'è ci_bo e vi_no.
There's food, and some wine here in this bas- ket.
CAV.
ANGEL.
Grazie!
Thank you.

(He urges Angelotti to hide in the chapel.)
CAV.
Pre_sto!
Hur- ry!
pp
CAV.
ANGEL.
Gra_zie!
Thank you.
Pre_sto!
Hur- ry!
pp
affrett:
TOSCA
(Annoyed.)
cres:
Ma - rio! Ma _ rio! Ma _ rio!
Ma - rio! Ma - rio! Ma - rio!
(Angelotti disappears in the chapel.)
(Opens the door with feigned calm.)
CAV.
Son
I'm
col canto

(Tosca storms in and loo'ks around suspiciously.)

*ANDANTINO SOST.to* ♩=56

CAV.

qui!
here.

*ANDANTINO SOST.to* ♩=56
*dolcissimo e con tutta l'espressione*

25

*pp*

(Cavaradossi wants to embrace her but she wards him off.)

CAV.

TOSCA

Perchè chiuso? (Pretending indifference.)
Why's the door locked?

CAV.

Lo vuole il Sa - gre - sta - no,..
The Sac- ris- tan in- sist - ed!

T.
CAV.
A chi par - la - vi? Al - tre pa - ro - le bi - sbi
I heard you speak - ing . . . No, no, I'm sure I heard some
A te!
To you!
- gliavi. Ov'è?... Colei!... Quella donna!.. Ho udito i lesti pas - si e
whis-p'ring. She's here. You know - that - wom-an! I heard a woman's step and the
Chi?
Who?
p
un fruscio di ve - sti... Lo ne - ghi?
rus-tling of a silk dress! De - ny it!
(With passion.)
So - gni!
Non-sense!
Lo nego e
I do! I
p cres.
f

(With a mild reproach.)
rit.
T.
Oh! in_nan_zi la Ma_don_na.
(Tries to kiss Tosca.) Oh, the Ho- ly Moth - er sees us.
CAV.
t'a - mo!
love you.
26
a tempo
dolcissimo
p col canto
ppp
(She walks slowly up to the Madonna
No, Mario mio, la_scia pria che la
No, Mar io, no! Let me of fer my
and places her flowers at the Madonna's feet.)
pre_ghi, che l'in_fio_ri...
prayers and my flow - ers.

(She kneels and offers a fervent prayer.)
T.
f
(She blesses herself and gets up.)
mf
dim.
pp poco rit:
(To Cavaradossi, who has returned to his work.)
AND. PIUTTOSTO LENTO
O_ra stammi a sentir... stas se ra
Can you meet me to-night? I've a per-
AND.te PIUTTOSTO LENTO
rall:

T.
can - to, ma è spet - ta - co - lo bre - ve. Tu m'a -
- form - ance but I'm through ver - y ear - ly. I'll ex -
mf
T.
- spet - ti sull'uscio della sce - na e al - la tua vil - la an - diam so - li, so -
- pect you as soon as it is o - ver and we will go a - way, you and I, to -
p
ALL.º VIVO
T.
- let - ti.
- geth - er.
MENO
È lu - na
There will be
CAVAR.
C.
(Who has been absent-minded.)
Stas - se - ra?!
This eve - ning?
27
ALL.º VIVO
MENO
mf
p

T.
pie_na e il not_tur_no ef_flu_vio flo_re_al i_ne_bria il
moon-light and the fra-grant per-fume of the night for us a-
pp
un poco rit:
pp
(She sits down at the foot of the dais close to Cavaradossi.)
T.
cor.
lone.
Non sei con_ten_to?
Won't that be love-ly?
m.d.
m.s.
LENTAMENTE
(Shocked by Cavaradossi's coolness.)
T.
Tornalo a dir!
Say it a-gain.
CAVAR. (Hardly paying attention.)
Tan_to!
Love-ly!
LENTAMENTE
mf
p
m.d.

Mosso
(Irritated.)
Lento
dolce
rall:
T.
Lo di_ci ma_le,
You do not mean it!
lo di_ci ma_le:
You do not mean it!
affrett.
CAV.
Tan_to!
Love - ly!
28
Mosso
Lento
mf
affrett.
f
p
pp
♩ = 116
Allegro mod.to
non la so_ spi_ri la no_stra ca_set_ta che tutta a_
Deep in the woods there's a house that will hide us, give us the
rit:
a tempo
_sco_sa nel ver_de ci a_spet_ta? ni_do a noi sacro, ignoto al
rest that the world has de_nied us. No one will find us in our

T.
mon - do in - ter, pien d'a - mo - re e di mi -
se - cret nest. Love a - lone will be our
mf
- ster? ......................
guest.
6
mf
p
p armonioso
allarg.
f
a tempo
Al tuo fian - co sen - ti - re per le si - len -
29
You and I, night and si - lence, crick - ets in the
allarg.
f
p
a tempo
- zïo - se stellate ombre, sa - lir le vo - ci del - le co - - -
gar - den, and high up - in - a tree a nightin - gale sing ing for you and

T.
se!..
me.
Dai
The
bo - schi e dai ro - ve - ti, dall'ar - se er - be, dal
sweet - est fra - grance bil - lows from trees and flow - ers. An
l'i - mo dei franti sepol - cre - ti odo - ro - si di ti - mo, la notte escon bi -
ar - bor a - midst the Weeping wil - lows will be our har - bor for lov - ers' se - cret
p
pp
rall.
stentando
sbi - gli di mi - nu - scoli a - mo - ri e per - fi - di con - si - gli
ses - sions, and the moon that dis - cov - ers those am - o - rous con - fes - sions
col canto
stentato

T.
che am - mol li - sco no i cuo - ri.
winks and smiles at the lov - ers.
6
mf
p
mf
p
T.
poco rit.
30
Fio - ri te o campi immen si, pal pi -
The stars will light our fac - es, and the
p poco rit.
a tempo
T.
ta - te au - re ma - ri - ne, au re ma -
night will be throb - bing with mu - sic a won - drous
a tempo
rit.
T.
ri - ne nel lu na re al bor,
sing - ing in the mid - night sky.
PP poco rit:
a tempo
m.d.

*espressivo*

T.

ah....... pio_vete volut_tà, volte stel_la_te! Ar_de in Tosca un folle a_

Ah, — you'll hold me in your passionate em-bra-ces, and the world will pass us

*f*

T.

_mor!

by.

*allarg. un poco* *a tempo*

*con anima*

CAVAR.

*f*

Ah!........................ M'av_vin_ci ne' tuoi

Ah! — you've en-slaved my heart for-

*con anima*

*cres.*

*f* *allarg. un poco* *a tempo*

(With complete abandon.)

T.

Arde a To_sca nel sangue il folle a_

I'm your To-sca, I'm yours for-ev-er-

*p dim:*...................... *pp*

CAV.

lac-ci mia si-re-na,

-ev-er. Love-ly To-sca!

*p dim.* *vellutato*

*pp*

(Resting her head on Cavaradossi's shoulder, who suddenly draws
rall.molto
pp
a tempo
T.
-mor!....
-more.
O mio amo-re!
I a-dore you.
CAV.
mia si-re-na,ver-rò!
How I long for to-night!
31
deciso
ppp
col canto.............
f
a tempo
back, looking towards the gate through which Angelotti disappeared.)
CAV.
Or la-sciami al la-
Now leave me to my
TOSCA
(Surprised.)
Mi di-scac-ci?
Must I leave you?
CAV.
-vo-ro.
paint-ing.
Ur-ge
It's the
p

(Gets up, annoyed.)
T.
CAV.
l'o - pra, lo sai!
pic - ture, you see.
Va_do,
Well then,
f
dim.
p
dolce rall:......... a tempo
va_do!..
ciao!
32
rall:.........
a tempo
f
(Moving away from Cavaradossi, then turning around she sees the
cres.
ff

painting and rushes back towards Cavaradossi in great agitation.)

T.
CAV.
-gl'occhi ci-le-stri-ni già li vi - di...
sky - blue eyes-I know I've seen them some - where.
(Nonchalantly.)
3
3
Ce n'è tan-ti pel
They are noth - ing un -
(Searching her memory.)
A - spet-ta...
Where was it?
A -
I
mon - do!..
- u - sual.
33
6
p
(Walks up the steps towards the picture.)
(Triumphantly.)
-spet-ta...
know her.
È l'At-ta-
It's L'At - ta -
mf
dim.
f

LO STESSO MOV.to AGITANDO UN POCO
(Overcome by jealousy.)
T.
-van - ti!,...
CAVAR. - van - ti!
La
She
(Laughs.)
Bra - va!..
Bra vo!
LO STESSO MOV.to AGITANDO UN POCO
f
p subito
(She cries.)
ve - di? T'a - ma? Tu l'a - mi? tu
knows you, loves you? You love her? You
l'a - mi?..
CAVAR. love her?
(Trying to calm her.)
Fu pu - ro ca - so...
I nev - er met her.
(Does not listen; furiously jealous.)
Quei pas - si
Those foot - steps...
f

*con anima*

*f*

T.

e quel bi - sbi - glio... Ah!..........
that se - cret whis - p'ring. Ah.

*f*

T.

...... Qui sta - - - va pur o - ra!..........
CAVAR. you saw her this morn - ing!

Vien
You're

*dim.*

*f*

(As a threat.)

T.

...... Ah! la ci - vet - ta! A me, a
You have be - trayed me! It's true, it's

CAV.

vi - a!
rav - ing

6

*ff*

*f*

T.
me!
true.
(Seriously.)
CAV.
La vi-di ie-ri, ma fu pu-ro ca-so.....
It's true, I saw her, yet I nev-er met her.
34
T.
Giu-ra!
Swear it!
CAV.
A pregar qui ven-ne...non vi-sto la ri-tras-si...
She came here to wor-ship; she nev-er e-ven saw me.
(With her eyes still on the painting.)
T.
Co-me mi guar-da fi-so! Di
Look how these eyes de-fy me! She
(Solemnly.)
CAV.
Giu-ro!
Glad-ly!
Vien vi-a...
Please go now!

(She walks backwards away from the picture with her hands in Cavaradossi's hands, but never taking her eyes off the picture.)
T.
me, bef - far - da, ri - de.
stares at me and mocks me.
(Gently urging Tosca to leave the dais.)
(Holding Tosca close
CAV.
Fol - li - a!
What non - sense!
(She gently upbraids him.)
rall.
AND.te SOSTENUTO
Ah, que-gli oc-chi!..
Ah, those eyes!
and looking into her eyes.)
Qua - l'oc-chio al mon - do può star di
I've nev er seen oth - er eyes so
35
p
armonioso
pa - ro al-l'arden-te oc - chio......... tuo ne - ro?...........
love - ly as your ar - dent dark eyes, my To - sca.

*con calore e cres.* *allarg.*

*p*

CAV.

È qui che l'es_ser mio, che l'es_ser mi _ o s'af_fi _ sa in_
Eyes that have seared my heart and have en - graved there your beau - ty for-

*cres.* *f* *col canto*

**Largamente**
*con grande espressione*

CAV.

_te _ ro.......... oc _ chio all'a_mor so _ a _ ve, al _ l'i _ ra
- ev - er. Eyes now a glow with pas - sion, now a - fire with

**Largamente**

*espressivo molto*

*p dolcissimo*

CAV.

fie _ _ _ _ _ ro.............. qual altro al mon _ do può star di
fu - - - - - - - ry. No oth - er eyes in this world can

*dolcissimo*

*p*

*rit.* *a tempo*

CAV.

pa _ ro al _ l'occhio tuo ñe _ _ _ _ _ ro?.......

ri - val your _ beau-ti - ful dark ___ eyes. ___

*pp* *rit:.........* *a tempo*

(Enraptured, she rests her head on his shoulder.)

*dolce, ma sentito ed espressivo*

TOSCA

*p*

Oh co_me la sai be _ _ _ ne l'ar _ te di farti a_

36 One word from you, my dar - ling, and I can doubt no

*p*

(With malice.)

*Lento*

T.

_ma _ _ re! Ma... fal_le gli occhi ne _ ri!..

long - er! But . . . won't you paint her eyes dark?

*Lento*

*rall:..................*

*p* *m.s.* *pp*

AND.te MOD.to
AND.te MOSSO 𝅗𝅥. = 60
T.
Sì, lo sen - to.... ti tor -
Yes, I'm guilt - y. I con-
CAVAR.
(Tenderly.)
Mia ge - lo - sa!
You are jeal - ous!
37
pp
tr
p
2 Ped.
- men - to sen - za po - sa.
fess that I am jeal - ous!
CAV.
Mia ge - lo - sa!
Love - ly To - sca . . .
Cer - ta so - no del per - do - no, cer - ta
Yet I'm cer - tain you'll for - give me. I am
Mia ge - lo - sa!
Jeal - ous To - sca.

poco rall: a tempo poco rit.
T.
so - no del per - do - no se tu guar - di al mio do -
sure you will for - give me when you know the grief in my
CAV.
Mia
My
f p
poco rall: a tempo poco rit.
a tempo
-lor!
heart.
To - sca ido - la - tra - ta, o - gni co - sa in te mi
To - sca, whom I wor - ship, who - a - lone makes life worth
p
a tempo
poco rall. a tempo
Cer - ta so - no del.... perdon se tu
I am sure you will for - give when you
pia - ce; l'i - ra au - da - ce e lo
liv - ing, I'll for - give you, for I
p

cres.
poco rit.
a tempo
T.
guar - di al mio do - lor!
know the grief in my heart.
CAV.
spa - si - mo d'a - mor!
know the grief in your heart.
poco rit.
a tempo
ff
dim.
p rall:
T.
Dil - la an-co - ra la pa-ro - la
Tell me love's un - end - ing sto - ry
sempre rall:
che con-so - la... dil - la an-co - ra!
in its glo - ry! Say you love me.
CAVAR.
Mia
My
sempre rall:
più

ANDte PASSIONALE
*con grande espressione*

CAV.

vi - ta, amante in quie - ta, di - rò sem - pre: «Flo - ria, t'a - mo!»
dar - ling, my be - lov - ed, do — be - lieve me. I a - dore you.

ANDte PASSIONALE
*con grande espressione*

38

*p*

*cres.* *allarg:* ............ *a tempo* *rall:* ............

CAV.

Ah! l'alma ac quie - ta, sempre «t'a - mo!» ti — di - rò!
This love I gave — you shall not die — un - til — I die.

*allarg:* ............ *a tempo*

*cres.* *f*

*p* *rall:* ............ *fp*

*fp*

TOSCA
(Drawing away from Cavaradossi.) *rall:* ............ *sempre più* ............

Dio! quante pecca - ta! M'hai tut - ta spetti - na - ta.
Oh, is noth - ing sa - cred? You see what you have done now?

CAV.

Or va,
But please,

*pp rall. sempre* ............

*ppp*

quasi a piacere
T.
Tu fi_no a stas_se_ra stai fer_mo al la_
You say you will work here all day at your
CAV.
la _ scia_mi!
leave me now!
pp
col canto
T.
_vo _ ro. E mi pro_met _ ti; sia ca_so o for_
paint - ing? Then you must prom - ise, that goes with out
rall:
stentate
T.
_tu _ na, sia treccia bionda o bru _ na, a pregar non ver_
say - - ing, no la - dy is to join you, no fair one and no
più rall.
T.
CAVAR. _ ra......... don_na nes _ su_na?
dark one, not e - ven pray - ing.
Lo giu_ro, amo_re!..
That is a pro - mise!

PIÙ LENTO ANCORA
(She falls into Cavaradossi's arms and offers him her cheek.)
T.
Quanto m'affretti!
Why do you rush me?
(With gentle reproach.)
No. perdo-na!..
Yes, I know it.
(Jokingly.)
CAV.
Va!
Please!
Anco-ra?
You prom-ised.
Davanti la Ma-donna?
Before the Ho-ly Moth-er?
39
ppp dolcissimo
(Moving her head towards the Madonna.)
(They embrace.)
(About to leave, she again looks at the picture and says maliciously.)
dolcissimo
È tan-to buo-na!
She's so for-giv-ing —
Ma fal-le gli occhi ne-ri!..
you'd bet-ter paint her eyes dark!
f allarg. pp
LENTAMENTE
(Quick exit.)
I° Tempo mosso
ppp
rall:
(Cavaradossi remains deep in thought.)
ppp
rall:
pppp

(Remembering Angelotti, he makes sure that Tosca has left, opens the door and, seeing that everything is quiet,

ALL.° AGITATO.
40
ff
p

he runs over to the chapel: Angelotti appears behind the gate. Cavaradossi opens it and they shake hands affectionately.)

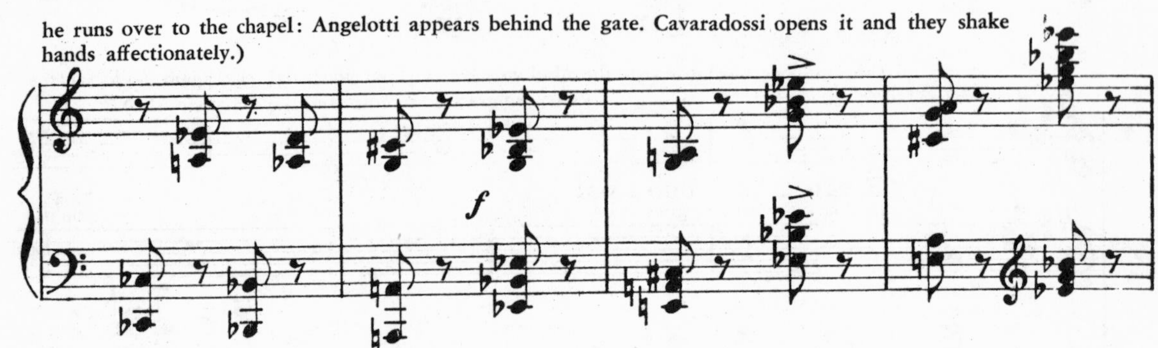
f

ff

(To Angelotti, who naturally must have heard the preceding conversation).

CAVAR.
È buo_na la mia
She's gen- er- ous, my
p

CAV.
To_sca, ma cre _ dente al con _ fes _ sor nulla tie _ ne ce-
To - sca, but she'll nev - er hide _ a _ thought from her fa - ther con-
dolce e legato
pp
CAV.
_la _ to, on _ d'io mi tacqui. È
-fes - - sor. I did not tell her. The
41
pp
p
f
p subito
CAV.
co - sa più pru _ dente.
less she knows the bet - ter!
ANGEL.
Siam so _ li?
The la - dy?

CAV.
Sì.
Gone.
Qua_l'è il vo_stro di_se_gno?..
First tell me what you're planning.
A.
A
Ac-
norma degli e_ven_ti, u_scir di Sta_to o
-cord-ing to e-vents, I'll leave the coun-try, or
A.
star ce_la_to in Roma....
stay in Rome in hid-ing.
Mia so_rel_la...
Now my sis-ter..

CAV.
L'At_ta _ van_ti?
L'At- ta- van- ti?
A.
Sì,...
Yes.
a _
She
42
p
_sco _ se un mu _ liebre abbiglia _ men - - to
hid an en- tire la- dy's ward - robe
m.s.
3
3
là sot_to l'al _ ta _ re....
there un- der the al- tar.
ve _ sti,
Man - tle,
sensibile e marcato

(Frightened, looks around.)
A.
ve_lo, ven_ta_glio...
bon-net, a fan, too!
43
misterioso
f
pp
A.
p
Ap _ pe _ na im _ bruni indos _ se _
To- night I'll get a- way dis-
CAVAR.
Or com_pren _ do!
Now I see it!
A.
_rò quei pan_ni....
-guised as a wo- man.
cres.

LO STESSO MOVIMENTO (in due)
CAV.
Quel fa - re cir - co
I saw her for a
LO STESSO MOVIMENTO (in due)
44
p
-spet - to......... e il pre - gan - te fer -
mo - ment here: she was kneel - ing and
-vo - - re in gio - vin don - na e
pray - ing. In one so young and
f
bel - - - la m'a - vean mes - so in so -
love - - - ly such fer - vor roused sus -
p cres.

CAV.
_spet _ to di qual _ che oc _ cul _ to a _
_pi _ cion: I thought she was in
incalzando
CAV.
_mor!... Or com_pren _ do!
love. Now I see it.
45
p
cres. e string.
CAV.
E _ ra a _ mor di so _ rel _ la!
It was love for a broth - er!
f
ff
ANGEL.
Tut_to el_la ha o _ sa _ to on _ de sottrarmi a
She'd stop at noth - ing to res-cue me from
f
ff

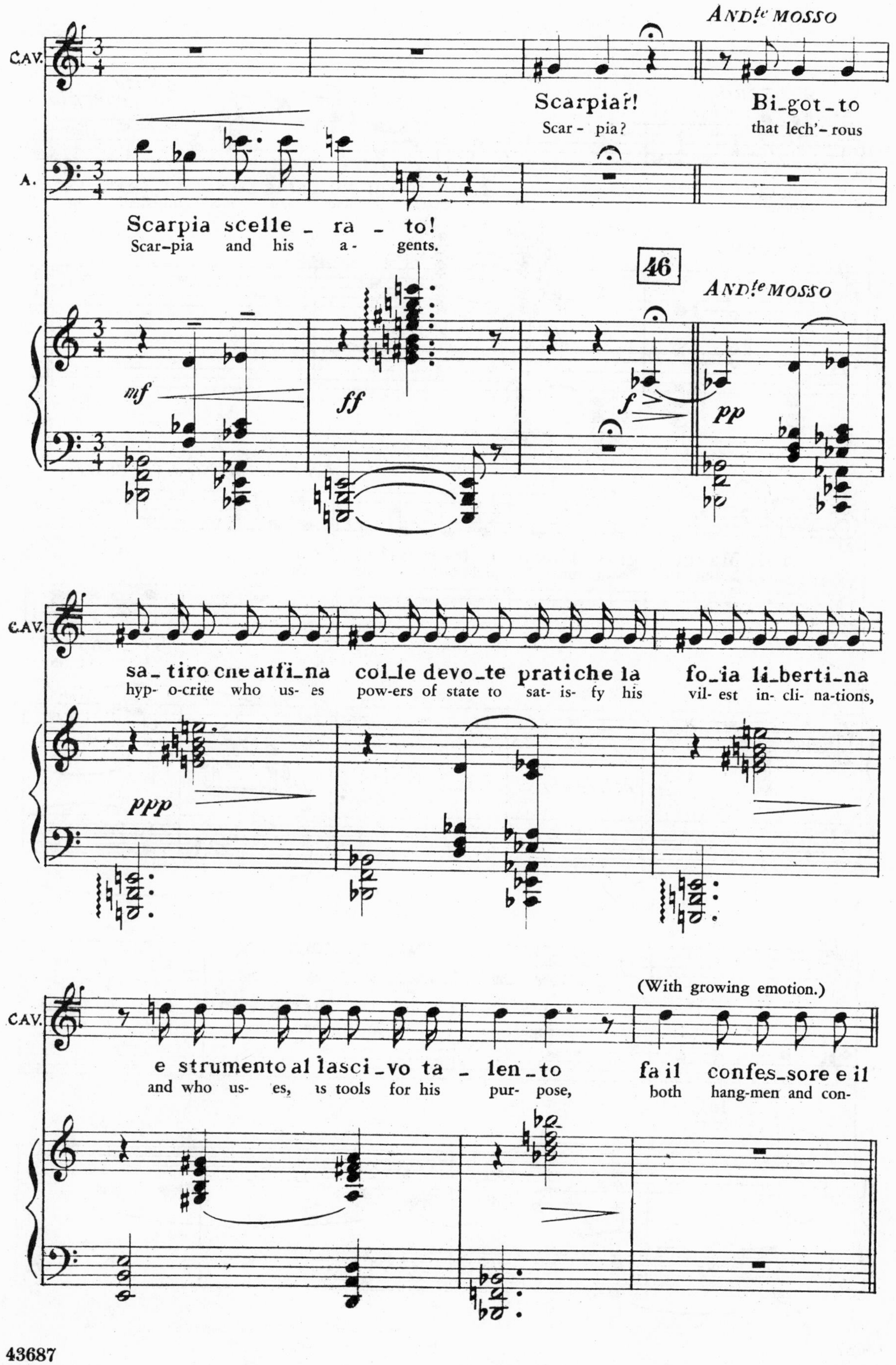

ANDte MOSSO

CAV. Scarpia?! Bi_got_to
Scar - pia? that lech'- rous

A. Scarpia scelle _ ra _ to!
Scar-pia and his a- gents.

**46** ANDte MOSSO

*mf* *ff* *f* *pp*

CAV. sa_tiro che affi_na col_le devo_te pratiche la fo_ia li_berti_na
hyp- o-crite who us- es pow-ers of state to sat- is- fy his vil- est in- cli- na-tions,

*ppp*

(With growing emotion.)

CAV. e strumento al lasci_vo ta _ len _ to fa il confes_sore e il
and who us- es, as tools for his pur- pose, both hang-men and con-

ALLEGRO
deciso
con energia
CAV.
bo_ia!
-fes-sor.
La vi_ta mi co_stas_se, vi sal_ve_
What-ev-er it may cost me, you shall be
ALLEGRO
ff
ff
UN POCO MENO del I° TEMPO
CAV.
_rò! Ma indu_giar fino a notte è mal si_cu_ro...
saved! But to wait un- til night-fall is im- pru-dent.
ANGEL.
Te_mo del
Yes, but in
col canto
p
CAV.
La cap_pel_la mette a un or_to mal
Right out there you'll find a door to a
A.
so_le!
day_light?

CAV.
chiuso, poi c'è un can_ne _ to che va lun_gi pei
gar- den. Look for a path - way through the sub - urbs that
CAV.
campi a una mia vil _ la... Ec _ co la
leads you to my vil - la. Here is the
ANGEL.
M'è nota...
I know it.
47
6
p
6
CAV.
chia _ ve... innanzi se_ra io vi rag_giungo, por-
latch key. I'll come and join you there this eve - ning. You
6
mf
6
p

CAV.
-ta - te con vo - i le ve - sti femmi - ni - li...
must take a - long all the clothes your sis - ter brought you.
p
f
(Angelotti picks up the bundle of clothes which his sister had hidden.)
AND.te LENTO
MOSSO COME PRIMA
PP dolce
Ped.
CAVAR.
Per or non
You do not
ANGEL.
Ch'io le in - dos - si?
Shall I wear them?
48
Vigoroso e deciso
p
f

CAV.
monta, il sen - tie - ro è de - ser - to...
have to You won't meet an - y - bod - y.
(About to leave.)
(Cavaradossi rushes over to Angelotti.)
ANGEL.
Ad - di - o!..
Till lat - er.
p
pp
2 Ped.
CAVAR.
a piacere
a tempo
Se urgesse il pe - riglio, correte al pozzo del giar - din.
If there's an - y - dan - ger, you can take shel - ter in the well.
col canto
pp a tempo
CAV.
a piacere
L'acqua è nel fon - do, ma a mezzo della canna un picciol varco
Deep down there's wa - ter but half - way up the shaft you will find a hid - ing
col canto

*a tempo*

CAV. guida ad un antro o_scu_ro, ri_fugio impenetra_bi_le e si_
place, big e_nough to hold you. If an_y-thing goes wrong, hide, as I

*a tempo* *col canto*

(A cannon-shot is heard: the two friends look at each other in alarm.)

*ALL.º VIVO*

CAV. _curo!
told you.

ANGEL. Il can_non del ca_
That's the gun at the

49 *ALL.º VIVO*

(cannone) *ff* *ff* *8ª sotto*

CAV. Fu sco_per_ta la fu_ga!
Your es_cape was dis_cov_ered.

A. _stello!..
Fort-ress!

*p cres.*

più cres. ancora ed incalz.
CAV.
Or Scarpia i suoi sbir - ri sguin - za - glia!
Now Scar - pia a lerts all his a - gents!
(Determined.)
CAV.
Con voi ver - rò. Staremo al -
I'll go with you. We'll stand to -
ANGEL.
Ad - di - o!
Till lat - er...
più cres. ancora ed incalz.
(Enthusiastically.)
(They rush away through the chapel.)
CAV.
- l'er - ta! Se ci as - sal - gon, bat - ta - glia!
- geth - er. We will live to de - feat them.
A.
O - do qual - cun!
I hear a step...
cres. ed incalz. sempre più

50
ff
m.s.
SAGR.
(Enters running, excited.)
Sommo giu_bilo, Eccel_
What ex - cite-ment! Ex- cel-
p
(Greatly surprised that once again he doesn't find the painter.)
rall.
Meno
rall. sempre
SAGR.
_len _ za!..
Nonc'è più!
Ne son do_lente!..
-len - cy!
He is gone.
Now that's a pit - y!
Meno
rall:.........
col canto..........
rall. sempre
più rall.
SAGR.
Chi con _ trista un mi_scre _ den _ te si gua_
If I ir- ri- tate a pa- gan I de-
più rall:.........

LENTO
rall:......
SAGR.
_dagna un' in_dul_genza!
- serve a small in- dul-gence.
LENTO
51
f deciso
rall:.....
ALL.° CON SPIRITO ♩.=132
SAGR.
Tut_ta
All you
RAGAZZI (Rushing in from all sides.)
CORO
CHIERICI, CONFRATELLI, ALLIEVI E CANTORI DELLA CAPPELLA
SOPRANI
TENORI
ALL.° CON SPIRITO ♩.=132
f

SAGR.
qui la can_to - ria! Presto!.. In sa_gre-
choir boys, come in. Hur-ry! Come in, I
(General confusion.)
Do_ve?
What for?
Do_ve?
What for?
Do_ve?
What for?
(Urging them towards the sacristy.)
(Out of breath.)
SAGR.
_stia.... Nol sa - pete? Bonaparte...
tell you! Don't you know yet? Bon-a-par-te . . .
Ma cheav_ven_ne?
What has hap-pened?
Ma cheav_ven_ne?
What has hap-pened?
Ma cheav_ven_ne?
What has hap-pened?

cres:........
SAGR.
scellerato...
that old scoundrel
Bonaparte...
Bon a - par - te . . .
Fu spen-
We at-
(Surrounding the Sacristan, while others rush in and join them.)
(tutti)
Ebben? Che fu?
Go on! Do tell.
Ebben? Che fu?
Go on! Do tell!
Ebben? Che fu?
Go on! Do tell!
p cres.
SAGR.
-na-to, sfra-cel-la-to e piom-ba-to a Bel-ze-bù!
-tacked him and we sacked him and we sent him back to hell!
Chi lo
And who
p cres.
p cres.

SAGR.
Ève_ri_dica pa - rola
It's the truth, you can be - lieve it.
È sogno! È fo_la!
We don't be- lieve it.
È sogno! È fo_la!
We don't be- lieve it.
di_ce?
says so?
52
p cres.
ff
SAGR.
or ne giunge la no_tizia!
I just heard the news this moment.
trattenuto
f
E questa
Yes, we shall
Sì fe_steggi la vit _to_ria!
There will be a cel- e- bra-tion!
Sì fe_steggi la vit _to_ria!
There will be a cel- e- bra-tion!
Sì fe_steggi la vit _to_ria!
There will be a cel- e- bra-tion!
mf
f tratto

tornando a tempo
SAGR.
se _ ra gran fiacco _ la _ ta, veglia di gala a Palaz_zo Far-
have _ a great cel- e- bra- tion. Scar - pia is giv - ing a ga- la re-
tornando a tempo
p
poco allarg:............ a tempo
SAGR.
_ne _ se, ed un' ap _ po_si_ta nuova can_
-cep- tion, and we shall hear, in a brand new can-
f p
dim.
SAGR.
_ta _ ta con Floria To _ sca!., E nelle
-ta- ta, Flo- ri - a To - sca! In all the
dim.
poco rall.
SAGR.
chie _ se in_ni al Si _ gnor!
church - es peo- ple will pray.
53
poco rall.
f a tempo

SAGR.
Or via a vestir_vi, non più clamor!
Put on your vest-ments and stop the noise.
Ragazzi
CORO
Soprani
Tenori
(Loudly.)
cres.
SAGR.
Via.... via.... in sagre - stia!
Go . . . go . . . go and get dressed.
(Giggling.)
Ah, ah, ah, ah, ah, ah, ah, ah, ah, ah!
Ah, ah, ah, ah, ah, ah, ah, ah, ah, ah! Dop_pio sol - do...
They'll pay dou - ble!
Ah, ah, ah, ah, ah, ah, ah, ah, ah, ah! Dop_pio sol - do...
They'll pay dou - ble!
54
cres.

(Laughing and shouting gaily, paying no attention to the Sacristan, who tries in vain to push

cres. sempre
Glo - ri - a! Vi - va il
Glo - ri a! Long live the
Te De - um... Glo - ri - a! Vi - va il
Te De - um Glo - ri a! Long live the
Te De - um... Glo - ri - a! Vi - va il
Te De - um Glo - ri a! Long live the
cres. sempre

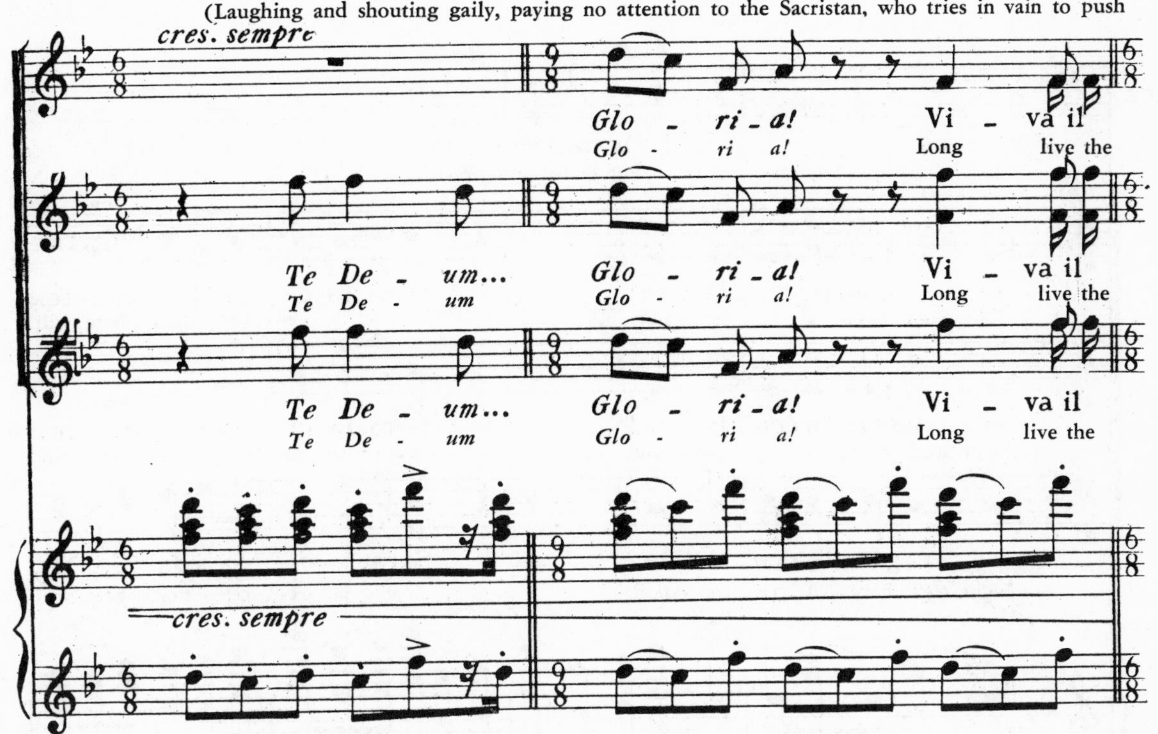

them towards the sacristy.)

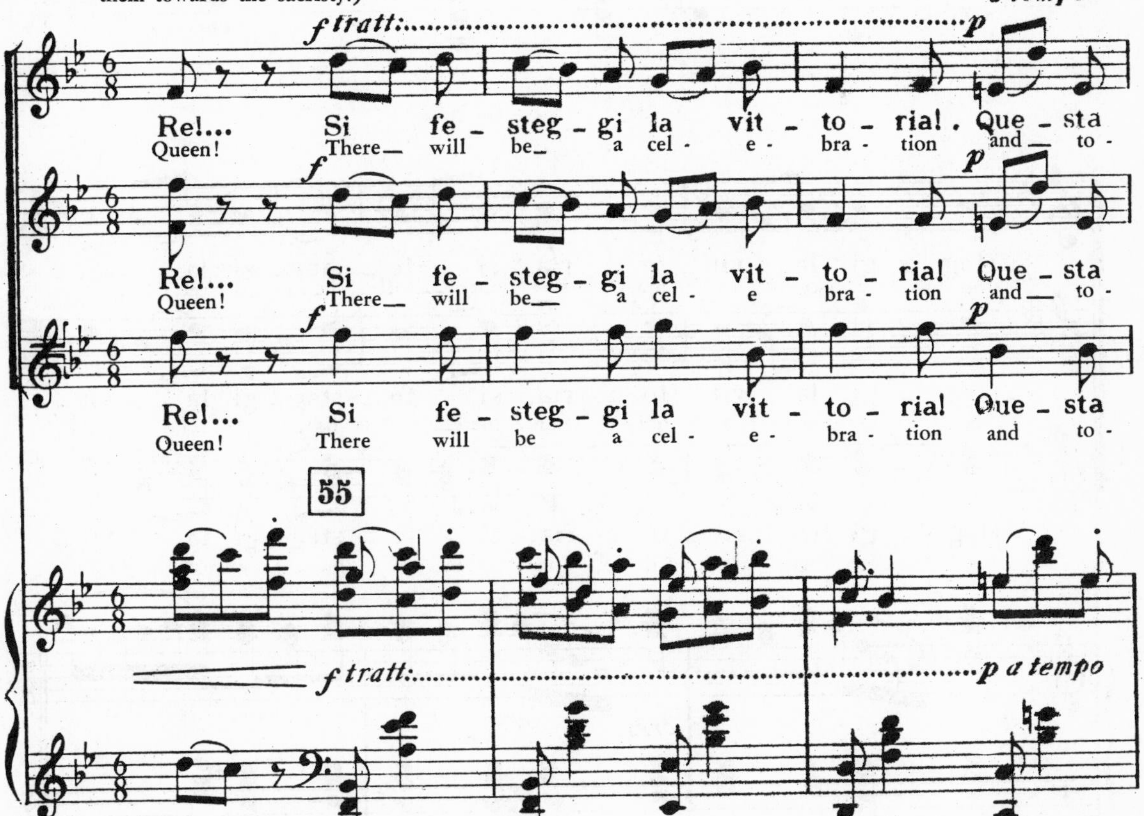

a tempo
f tratt: p
Re!... Si fe - steg - gi la vit - to - ria! Que - sta
Queen! There will be a cel - e - bra - tion and to -
f p
Re!... Si fe - steg - gi la vit - to - ria! Que - sta
Queen! There will be a cel - e bra - tion and to -
f p
Re!... Si fe - steg - gi la vit - to - ria! Que - sta
Queen! There will be a cel - e - bra - tion and to -
55
f tratt: p a tempo

SAGR.
f
Or via a ve_stirvi!...
Put on your vestments.
se _ ra gran fiacco_la_ta!
- night we'll have a re - cep - tion.
Sera_ta di ga _ la! Si fe-
A ga- la re- cep - tion. There will
f
cres.
_steg - gi la vit - to - ria, si fe - steg - gi la vit_
be a cel e - bra - tion, there _ will be _ a cel - e -
cres.

(Jumping and laughing.)
to - ria! Vi - va il Re! Vi - va il Re!
bra - tion! Long live the Queen! Long live the Queen!
56
ff
Te Deum.... Glo - ria! Si fe - steg - gi la...... vit -
Te-Deum . . . Glo - ria! There will be — a vic - to - ry

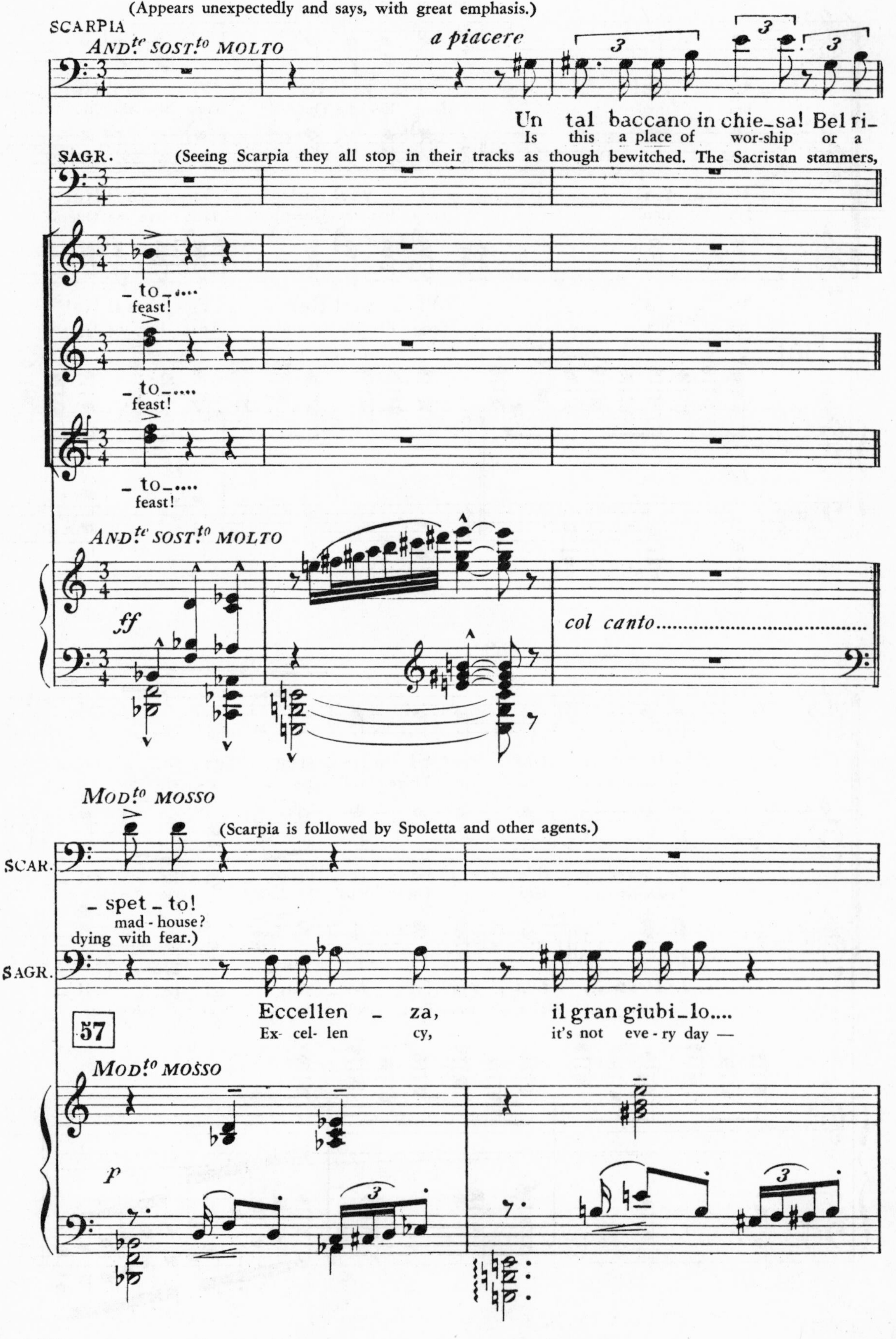
(Appears unexpectedly and says, with great emphasis.)
SCARPIA
AND.te SOST.to MOLTO
a piacere
Un tal baccano in chie_sa! Bel ri-
Is this a place of wor-ship or a
SAGR.
(Seeing Scarpia they all stop in their tracks as though bewitched. The Sacristan stammers,
_to_....
feast!
_to_....
feast!
_to_....
feast!
AND.te SOST.to MOLTO
ff
col canto
MOD.to MOSSO
(Scarpia is followed by Spoletta and other agents.)
SCAR.
_spet_to!
mad-house?
dying with fear.)
SAGR.
Eccellen _ za, il gran giubi_lo....
Ex- cel- len cy, it's not eve-ry day —
57
MOD.to MOSSO
p

(All slink away quietly; the Sacristan, too, hopes to disappear but Scarpia brusquely orders him to stay.)
SCAR.
Apprestate per il Te Deum.
Go, get ready for the Te- Deum.
Tu
You
p
(To Spoletta.)
resta!
stay here.
E tu va, fruga ogni angolo, raccogli ogni
And you there, take a few men with you and search eve-ry
SAGR.
(Frightened, humbly.)
Non mi muovo!
At your or-ders.
pp
SPOLETTA
(Orders two agents to follow him.)
Sta be-ne!...
At once, sir!
(To the other agents, who do as they are told.)
trac-cia!
cor- ner!
Occhio alle por- te, sen-za dar so-
Watch eve-ry ex- it. Don't at-tract at-

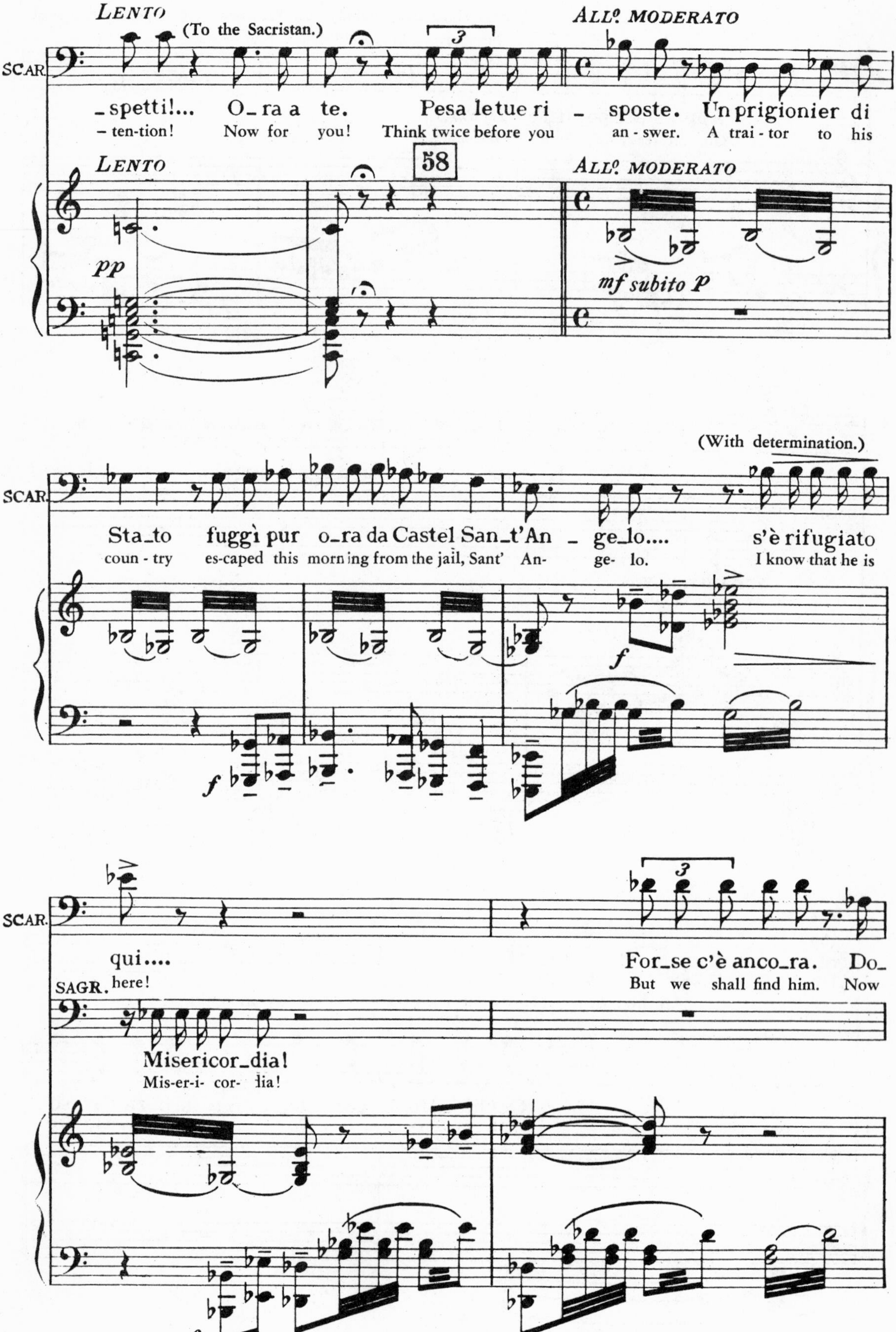

LENTO (To the Sacristan.) ALL.º MODERATO

SCAR.

-spetti!... O-ra a te. Pesa le tue ri - sposte. Un prigionier di

- ten-tion! Now for you! Think twice before you an - swer. A trai - tor to his

LENTO 58 ALL.º MODERATO

pp mf subito p

(With determination.)

SCAR.

Sta-to fuggì pur o-ra da Castel San-t'An - ge-lo.... s'è rifugiato

coun - try es-caped this morning from the jail, Sant' An- ge- lo. I know that he is

f f

SCAR.

qui.... For-se c'è anco-ra. Do-

here! But we shall find him. Now

SAGR.

Misericor-dia!

Mis-er-i- cor- dia!

f

SCAR
-v'è la cappel-la degli Atta-van-ti?
which one is the At- ta- van- ti chap- el?
(Walks over to the gate,
SAGR.
Ec - cola!...
There it is.
pesante
finding it ajar.)
SAGR.
A - per - ta! Ar - can - ge - li!
It's o - pen! For good- ness sakes!
(Thev enter the chapel but return at once: Scarpia, annoyed, holds a fan in his hands which he toys with nervously.)
SCARPIA
Buon indizio....
That's sus-pi-cious.
Entriamo.
Let's en- ter.
SAGR.
E un'altra chiave!
This is not, my key!
lunga
dim.
pp

AND.te LENTO
(Speaking to himself.)
SCAR.
59
Fu grave sba_glio quel colpo di can_no_ne. Il ma_ri_
It was an er- ror to have that cannon fired. It on-ly
AND.te LENTO
pp
sf
_o_lo spiccato ha il vo_lo, ma lasciò u_na pre_da... pre-
gave him a time-ly warn-ing. But he left me a keepsake... the
legato
cres. e sempre legato
sf
(Gesturing with the fan.)
ALL.o SOST.to MOLTO
_zio_sa.... un ven_ta_glio.
scoun-drel left this fan here!
60
ff
pesante
Qual com_plice il mi_sfat_to pre_pa_
I won- der who the fair ac- com-plice

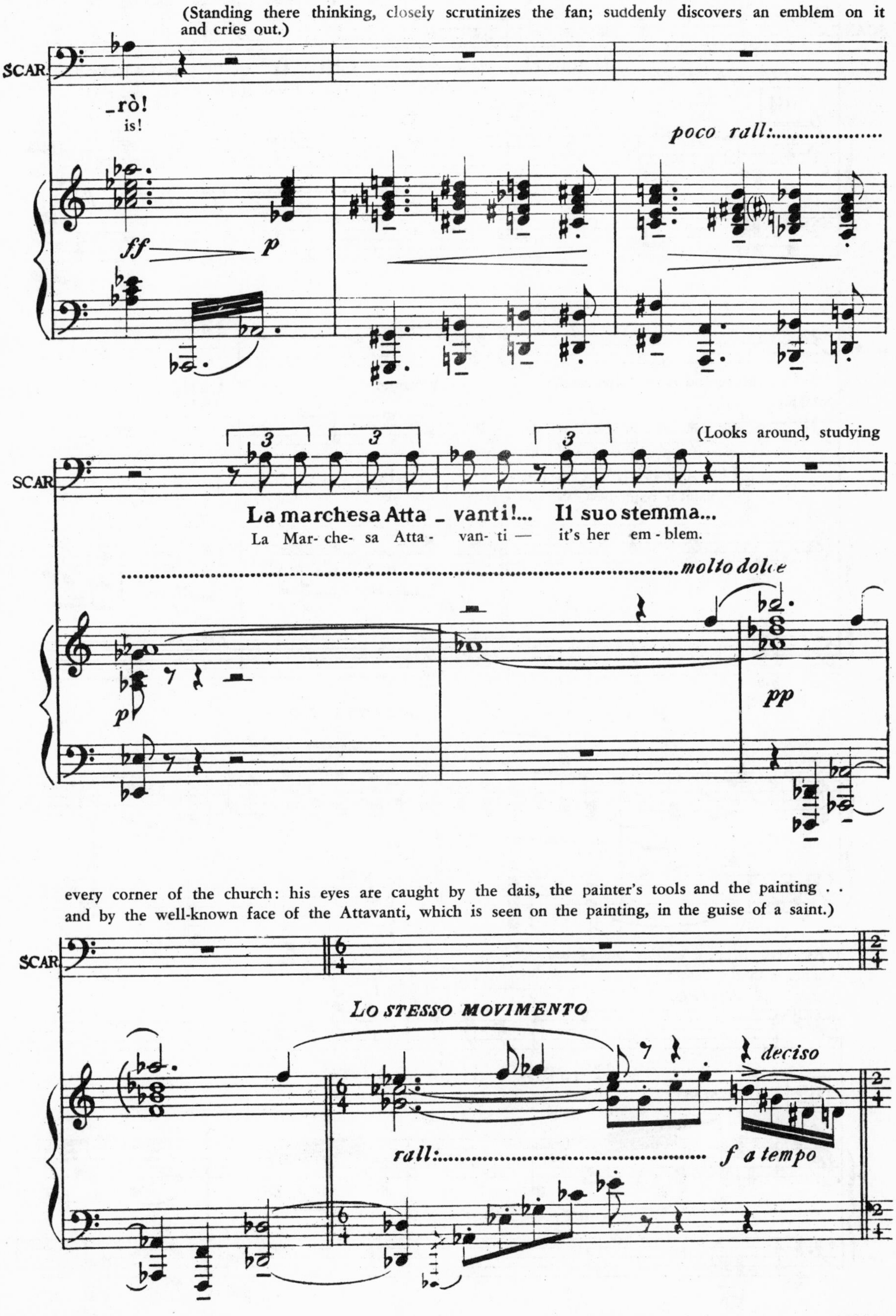

(Standing there thinking, closely scrutinizes the fan; suddenly discovers an emblem on it and cries out.)

SCAR.

-rò!
is!

*poco rall:*

*ff* *p*

SCAR.

La marchesa Atta - vanti!... Il suo stemma...
La Mar- che- sa Atta- van- ti — it's her em - blem.

*molto dolce*

*p* *pp*

(Looks around, studying every corner of the church: his eyes are caught by the dais, the painter's tools and the painting . . and by the well-known face of the Attavanti, which is seen on the painting, in the guise of a saint.)

ALL? CON MOTO
(To the Sacristan.)
SCAR.
Il suo ri _ trat_to! Chi fe' quelle pit_tu_re?
This is her pic - ture! You know the man who did this?
ALL? CON MOTO
61
col canto
f
SCAR.
(More and more frightened.)
a tempo
Lui!
He!
SAGR.
Il ca_valier Ca_vara _ dossi...
A painter named Ca - va - ra - dos- si.
p
SOSTENENDO
f
(Discovers an agent coming out of the chapel with the basket.)
SAGR. A TEMPO
Nu_mi! Il pa _ niere!
Mer - cy, that's the bas - ket.
62
A TEMPO
f

43687

(Continuing his trend of thought.)

SCAR.

Lui! L'aman_te di
He! The lov- er of

SCAR.

cres.

To_sca! Un uom so_spet_to! Un vol_ter_
To-sca! A friend of trai-tors... per-haps a

cres.

SCAR.

_rian!
spy.

(After peering into the basket, he cries in great surprise.)

SAGR.

Vuoto?.. Vuoto!..
Emp-ty, emp-ty!

ff f più f

(Seeing the agent with the basket.)
SCAR.
Che hai det_to? Che fu?..
What is it? Speak up!
(Taking the basket from the agent.)
SAGR.
Si ri_tro_
How did it
ff
dim.
Più mosso
SCAR.
Tu lo co_no_sci?..
You know the bas-ket?
SAGR.
_vò nella cappella questo pa_nier.
get in-to the chap-el? I'd like to know.
63
Più mosso
p
f
p
SAGR.
Cer_to! È il ce_sto del pit_
Sure-ly, I see it eve-ry
f
p
f
p

*con forza, quasi parlato*

SCARPIA

Sputa quello che
Tell me all that you

(Stammers with fear.)

SAGR.

-tor... ma... non-di-me-no...
day. But all the same I...

*f* *p*

SCAR.

sai.
know.

(Still more frightened, almost crying, he shows him the empty basket.)

SAGR.

Io lo la-sciai ri-pie-no di
I al-ways leave this bas-ket when

*f* *p* *poco accel.* *p*

*poco rall.*

SAGR.

*a tempo*

ci-bo pre-li-ba-to... il pran-zo del pit-
ev-er he is paint-ing — it's just a bit of

*poco rall:* ........ *a tempo*

*pp*

SCARPIA
(Continuing his inquiry to discover new clues.)
A_vrà pran_za_to!
That means he ate here.
SAGR.
_tor!..
lunch.
Nel_la cap_pel_la?
There in the Chap-el?
64
p
pp
(Indicating "no" by a gesture.)
poco rit.
Non ne ave_a la chia_ve nè con_ta_va pran_zar... disse egli
But how did he get in there? And he want-ed no food, that's what he
legato
poco rit.
p
a tempo
(Showing where he left the basket and putting it there.)
stesso. Ond'io l'avea già mes_so.......... al ri_pa_ro.
told me. There-fore I set it down here by the plat-form.
p

(Impressed by the severe silence of Scarpia, mumbling to himself.)

SAGR.
(Li_bera me Domine!)
pp
dim.
SCARPIA
(pausa)
p (To himself.)
(Or tutto è chia_ro............ la prov_vi_sta del sa_
I—see it clear-ly; with the food the paint-er
65
(pausa)
p
cres.
SCAR.
-cri_ _sta d'An_ge_lot_ _ti fu la
left un- touched, An- ge- lot- ti stilled his—
f

SCAR.
pre-da!)
hun-ger.
66
f cres.
ff

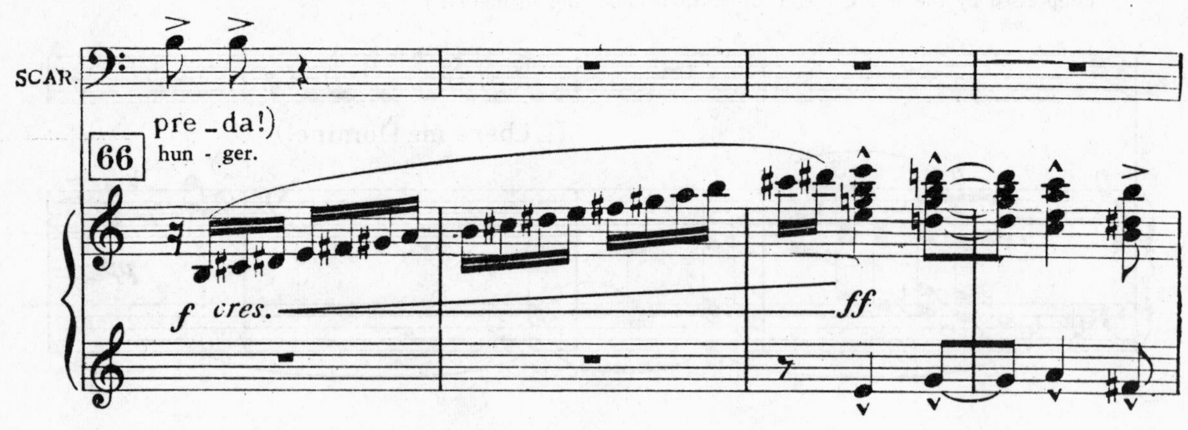

(Tosca returns in a state of great excitement: walks up to the dais and, not finding Cavaradossi, rushes all about the church looking for him. Scarpia, on seeing Tosca, quickly hides behind the column near the holy water basin, beckoning to the Sacristan to stay. Trembling, he approaches the painter's dais.)

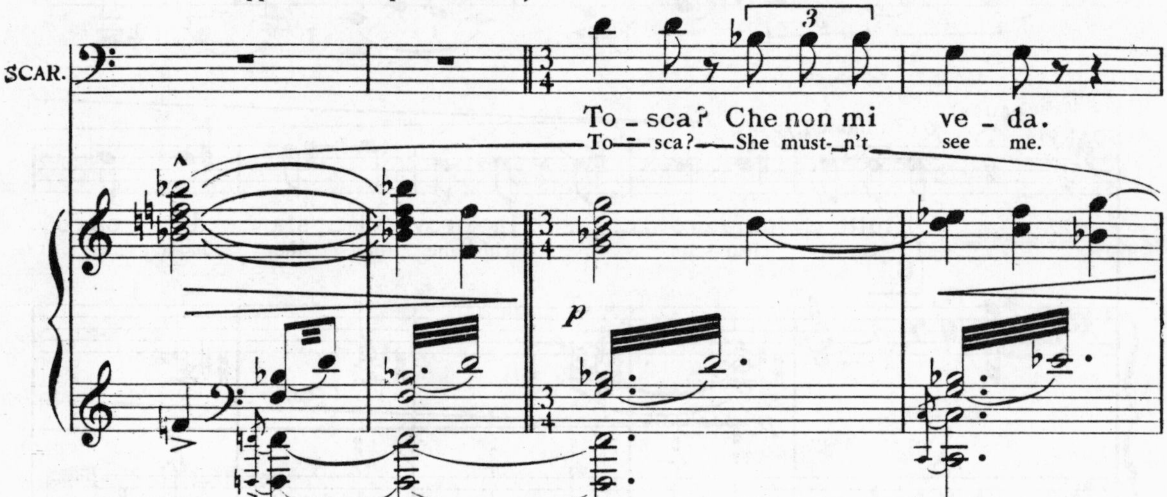

SCAR.
To-sca? Che non mi ve-da.
To-sca? She must-n't see me.
p

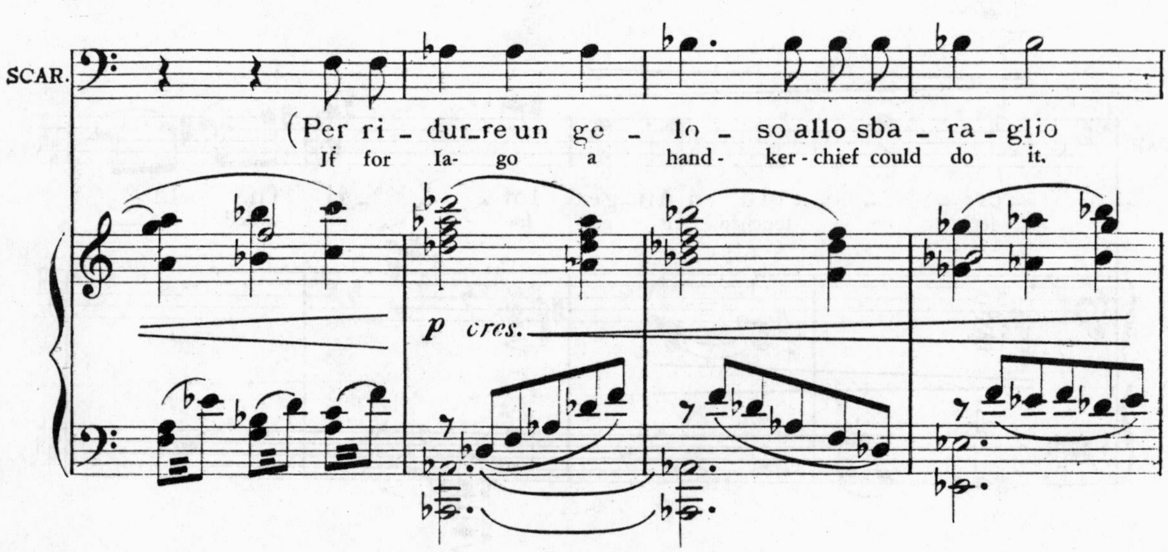

SCAR.
(Per ri-dur-re un ge-lo-so allo sba-ra-glio
If for Ia-go a hand-ker-chief could do it,
p cres.

(Walking back to the dais,
poco allarg.
ALLEGRO
SCAR.
Ja-go ebbe un fazzo-let-to... ed io un ven-taglio!..)
may- be a la-dy's fan will work for Scar-pia!
ALLEGRO
67
she cries out impatiently.)
TOSCA
Ma-rio?!
Ma- rio!
Ma-rio?!
Ma- rio!
(Walking up to Tosca.)
SAGR.
Il pit-tor Cava-ra-dossi? Chi
If you want Ca-va-ra- dos-si, you're
ff
f p subito
SAGR.
sa do-ve sia? Sva-nì, sgatta-io-lò per sua stregone-
call-ing in vain. He's here, and then be-fore you look, he's gone a-
dim.
cres.

TOSCA
Ingan - na - ta? No... no...
(Hurries away.) He's de - ceived me? No, no,
SAGR.
- ria.
- gain.
mf
dim.
ANDte MOSSO ♩= 100
(Almost crying.)
T.
tra - dir - mi e - gli non può, tra - dirmi egli non
I know he's faith - ful to me. I know that he is
68
Campane
ANDte MOSSO ♩= 100
p
T.
può!
true!
(To Tosca, with gentle insinuation.)
SCARPIA
p
To - sca di -
If I may
p
p

SCAR.

-vi_na la ma_no mia la vo_stra a_spet_ta, picco_la ma-

lin-ger and take your hand, I won't car- ess you, on-ly touch your

SCAR.

-ni_na, non per galante_ri_a, ma........... per offrir_vi

fin-ger, not in a worldly spir- it, but offring ho-ly

TOSCA

(Touches Scarpia's fingers and blesses herself.)

Gra_zie, si_gnor!

You're ver- y kind.

SCAR.

l'acqua bene_det_ta...

wa-ter that will bless you.

69

*dolce*

*pp*

poco rall.
a tempo
SCAR.
Un no _ bile e_sempio è il vo _ _ stro. Al cie _ lo
I wish there were more as no - ble as you! Your sing - ing
dolce ma sensibile
poco rall.
P a tempo
SCAR.
pie - na di san - to ze_lo attin_ge _ te del_l'ar_te il ma _ gi -
sets all the heav - ens ringing and your art, far from be - ing vain and
TOSCA
(Absent-mindedly.)
(A few people are seen slowly entering
Bon_tà vostra...
You're too gen-'rous.
p
SCAR.
_stero che la fe - de rav_vi _ va!
i - dle, is an act of de - vo - tion.
Le pie don_ne son
But I know what I'm
pp
pp

the church.)
(With obvious intent.)
SCAR.
rare...Voi calca _ te la scena...e in chiesa ci ve_ni _ te per pre _
saying: when on stage you are playing, but when you come to church, you come to
mf
TOSCA
(Surprised.)
Che inten_dete?..
You're im- ply-ing? . . .
SCAR.
_gar...
pray.
E non fa_te come cer_te sfron.
When you're kneeling you ex-press what you're
Campane
70
p
mf
cres.
p
(Pointing to the painting.)
(Making his meaning quite clear.)
poco rall:
SCAR.
_tate che han di Maddalena viso e co_stumi...
feel-ing. Oth- ers tho they look like the Holy Ma_donna,
e vi tre_scand'amo_re!
real-ly come to meet their lov-ers.
f

ALL° MODERATO
TOSCA
(Wincing.)
Che? D'a_more?
What, what lov-ers?
Le prove! Le prove!
Sus-pi-cions! But prove it!
71
ALL° MODERATO
f
subito p
(Grasping it.)
(Some peasants are seen entering.)
T.
Un ventaglio? Dove stava?
Let me see it. And where was it?
(Showing her the fan.)
SCARPIA
È arne_se di pit_to_re questo?
Since when is this a tool of paint-ers?
Là su quel
Here by his
sf
SCAR.
pal_co.
scaf-fold.
Qualcun venne
Some-one must have
72
p

poco affrett:
SCAR.
cer_to a sturbar gli a_manti ed es_sa nel fug - gir per_dè le
come to dis-turb the love-birds. The fe-male flew a - way and lost some
p poco affrett:...
(Looking over the fan.)
TOSCA
a tempo
La corona! Lo stemma! È l'Atta - van - ti!
L'At-ta-van-ti! Her em-blem... The At-ta - van - ti!
SCAR.
pen_ne!..
feath-ers.
a tempo
ff
ff
(With great feeling, hardly able to hold back
T.
Pre_sa_go so - spetto!..
A-gain that sus- pi- cion!
Ed
To
SCAR.
(Ho sor_ti_to l'ef - fet_to!)
I have made an im- pres-sion.
73
f

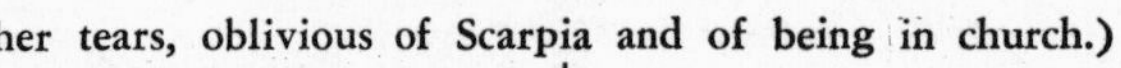
her tears, oblivious of Scarpia and of being in church.)

AND.te MESTO ♩= 40
T.
io ve_ni_vo a lui tut_ta do_glio_sa
per
think my poor de- lud-ed heart was bleed-ing
for
AND.te MESTO ♩= 40
P con espressione

T.
dir_gli: in_van stas_se_ra il ciel s'in_fo_sca
fear that I might hurt him if I told him

Sostenuto molto
con grande passione
T.
l'in_na_mo_ra_ta To_sca è pri_gio_
to- night his lov-ing To-sca would de-
74
Sostenuto molto
f

T.
-nie - ra......................
SCARPIA- sert him
(Già il ve-le - no l'ha ro-sa...)
(How my plan is suc-ceed-ing!)
p
poco rit.
T.
dei re-ga-li tri-pu-di, pri-gio-nie - - -
would be forced by her du-ties to de-sert
pp
cres.
f pp poco rit.
(Shepherds and peasants are seen in the background.)
T.
-ra!..
SCARPIA him . . .
(Già il ve-le - no l'ha ro-sa.)
(Yes, my plan is suc-ceed-ing.)
p

(In honeyed tones.)
I.º Tempo
SCAR.
75
O che v'of _ fen _ de, dol _ ce si_
What makes you trem- ble, most gra-cious
Campane
I.º Tempo
p
SCAR.
_gno _ ra?..
la - dy?
U_na ri_bel_le la_crima
You can-not hide the tears that are
p
SCAR.
pp
scen_de sovra le bel_le guancie e le ir _ ro _ ra; dol _ ce si _
steal- ing out of your eyes: they sim- ply won't let you, most gra-cious

rall. molto
a tempo
SCAR.
-gnora, che mai v'ac - co-ra?
la- dy. What has up - set you?
p
TOSCA
AND.te LENTO
(Some noblemen, accompanied by their ladies, enter the church.)
Nul-la!
Noth-ing!
(With emphasis.)
rall.
SCAR.
76
Da-rei la vi - ta per a-sciugar quel
These bit - ter tears, I would give my life to
AND.te LENTO
rall:
MENO
(Does not listen to Scarpia.)
T.
Io qui mi strug-go e in - tan-to d'altra in
Here I am, suf - f'ring and cry - ing, while he's
SCAR.
pian - to.
dry them.
MENO
pp

T.
braccio le mie sma_nie de - ri - de!
laugh - ing in the arms of an - oth - er!
SCAR.
(Morde il ve - le - no.)
(Just as I planned it.)
dim.
(Very bitterly.)
T.
77
Do_ve son?
If I knew!
pp
(Some more citizens are sauntering in.)
cres.
T.
Potes_si coglierli i tra_di - to_ri.
But I will catch them yet both to - geth - er!
cres.

(More and more upset.)
con forza
cres.
T.
Oh qual so-spet-to!
Ah, what a vi-sion:
Ai dop-pi a-
to find I'm
T.
-mo-riè la vil-la ri-cet-to.
right in that dread-ed sus-pi-cion!
f
(In ever greater grief.)
T.
Tradi-tor,...
I'm be-trayed,
tradi-tor!
I'm be-trayed.
rall:
dim.
pp

ALLº VIVO
con forza
T.
Oh mio bel nido insozza_to di fan_go!
Our nest be- fouled by his cheating and ly- ing.
78
ff
(With a quick resolve.)
(Turns to the painting with a menacing gesture.)
Vi piom_berò inat_te_sa!
But I will not al- low it!
(With a desperate outcry.)
Tu non l'avrai stas_se_ra. Giuro!
You'll nev- er have your lov- er, I swear it!
(Shocked; as though reproaching her.)
SCARPIA
In chie_sa!
Blas- phem-ing?

(Crying.)
MENO
LENTO
con grande espressione
rall.
ten.
Dio mi per - do - na...
God will for - give me
Egli vede ch'io
when He sees how I'm
MENO
LENTO
pp
pp
rall.
col canto
cres.
AND.te SOST.to
(Crying bitterly.)
(Scarpia offers her his arm, sees her
pian - go!.......
cry - ing.
AND.te SOST.to
79
p
cres. molto
ff
p
to the door, pretending to comfort her.)

f
f
(After Tosca's departure, more and more people stream into the church.)
p
pp
80
(Scarpia, having accompanied Tosca, returns to the column; at his sign Spoletta appears suddenly.)
AND.te MOSSO
rall.
ff energico, tutta forza
rall:..............
pp
(The crowd gathers in the background waiting for the cardinal; some kneel and pray.)
SCARPIA
LARGO RELIGIOSO SOST.to MOLTO 𝅗𝅥 = 42
cupo
3
3
3
Tre sbirri... Una carrozza...
Spo - let - ta, follow that la - dy.
LARGO RELIGIOSO SOST.to MOLTO 𝅗𝅥 = 42
(Campane)

SCAR.
Pre_sto... seguila dovunque va_da... non vi_sto... prov
Hur ry! Do not a-rouse her sus- pi- cion . . . a car-riage . . be
legato, cupo
pp
sostenute le terzine
SPOL.
(Spoletta rushes off.)
Sta bene. Il con_vegno?
I shall be. Where'll I find you?
SCAR.
_ve_di!
care-ful!
Palazzo Far_nese!
Pal-az- zo Far- nese.
(With a sardonic smile.)
SCAR.
Va, To_sca!
Go, To-sca!
m.d.
p

SCAR.
p
Nel tuo cuor s'anni - da Scar - pia...
Don't for - get the name of Scar pia!
3
3
3

(The cardinal, accompanied by the crowd, goes to the high altar; the Swiss guards keep the crowd in line.)

SCAR.
(Ironically.)

Va, To - sca!
Go, To - sca!

81

ORGANO p

Pedale

p

SCAR.

È Scarpia che sciogli e a volo il fal - co della tua ge - lo -
And Scar - pia, re - mem - ber has been the one who roused you to jeal - ous

legato
pp

f

✻ Cannone

SCAR.
- si - a.
pas - sion.
82
Quanta pro_mes _ sa
All your sus- pi- cions
pietto semplice
mf
ORGANO
legato
p
sempre sosten.
le terzine
✻Cannone
SCAR.
nel tuo pron_to so _ spet_to!
are to me full of prom - ise!
senza pedale
✻Cannone

SCAR.

Nel tuo cuor s'anni - da Scarpia....
Don't for - get the name of Scar-pia;

(Ironically.)

(Scarpia kneels and prays as the cardinal passes.)

SCAR.

Va, To - sca!
Go, To - sca!

ff

mf

m.s.

83

più p



※ Cannone

(The cardinal blesses the kneeling congregation.)
SCAR.
con voce parlata
Ragazzi e Sop.i
Qui fe_cit cœlum et
Tenori
Qui fe_cit cœlum et
Bassi
Qui fe_cit cœlum et
FOLLA
con voce parlata
12 Bassi
Adjutorum nostrum in nomine Domini
CAPITOLO
solo, pieno semplice
pedale
legato
più p

(Ferociously.)
SCAR.
A dop - pia mi - ra
Mine is the pow - er,
terram
84
Et hoc nunc et usque in
terram
Et hoc nunc et usque in
terram
Et hoc nunc et usque in
Sit nomen Do_mi_ni be_ne _ dictum
84

SCAR.

ten - - do il vo - ler, nè il capo del ri -
two - fold is my aim: to see a trai - tor

*saeculum.*

*saeculum.*

*saeculum.*

SCAR.

- bel - - le è la più pre - zïo - - sa .........
hang - - ing is by no means the great - er one.

SCAR.

Ah di que_gli oc_chi vit_to_
Soon I shall see her with her

85

pp

Cannone

SCAR.

_rïo_si ve_der......... la fiam_ _ma
eyes all a_fire in pas_ sion;

(Passionately excited.)

CAR.

il - lan - gui - dir con spa - si - mo — d'a -

flam - ing de - light, her bod - y trembling with

mf cres.

pedale

p cres.

3

※ Cannone

SCAR.

- mor fra le mie brac - cia

love in my em - brac - es!

f

f

dim.

86

m.s.

f

※ Cannone

dim.

(Wildly.)

SCAR.

il_lan_gui_dir d'a_mor.................. L'u_no al ca_
Both of them shall be mine: ______ one on the

*Cannone

SCAR.

_pe_stro, l'al_tra fra le mie brac_cia.....
gal-lows and the oth-er in Scar-pia's arms!

(The entire congregation has turned towards the altar; some kneel.)

CORO

Ragazzi e Sop! Te

Tenori Te

Bassi Te

(Motionless, he stares into thin air.)
SCAR.
87
Deum
la - u - - da - - -
Deum
la - u - da - - -
Deum
la - u - - da - - -
Campane
3
ff
87
3
Cannone

SCAR.
-mus: te.......... Do - mi-num con - fi -
-mus: te.......... Do - mi-num con - fi -
-mus: te.......... Do - mi-num con - fi -
3
❋ Cannone

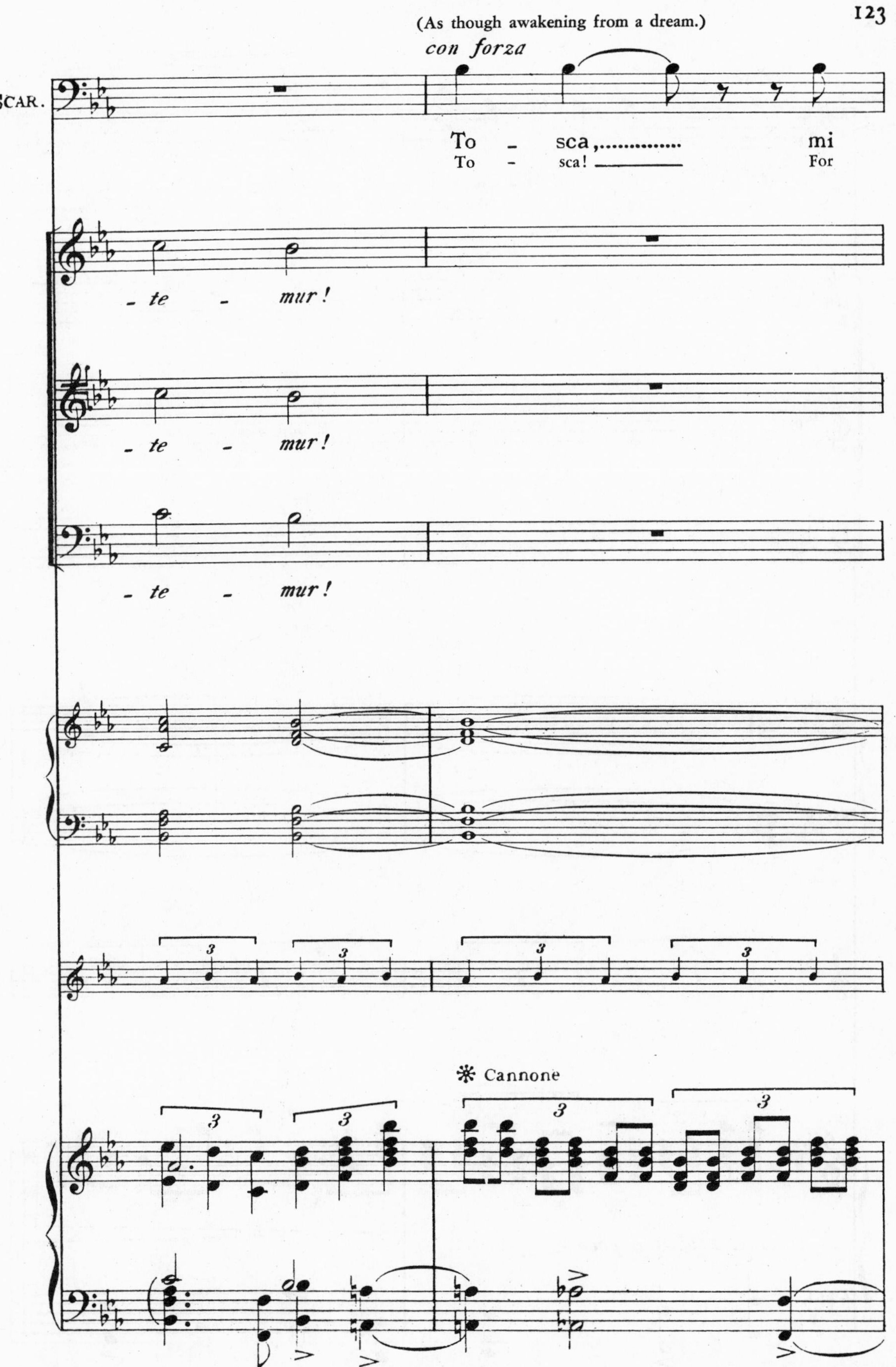
(As though awakening from a dream.)
con forza
SCAR.
To - sca, ............... mi
To - sca! For
- te - mur!
- te - mur!
- te - mur!
Cannone

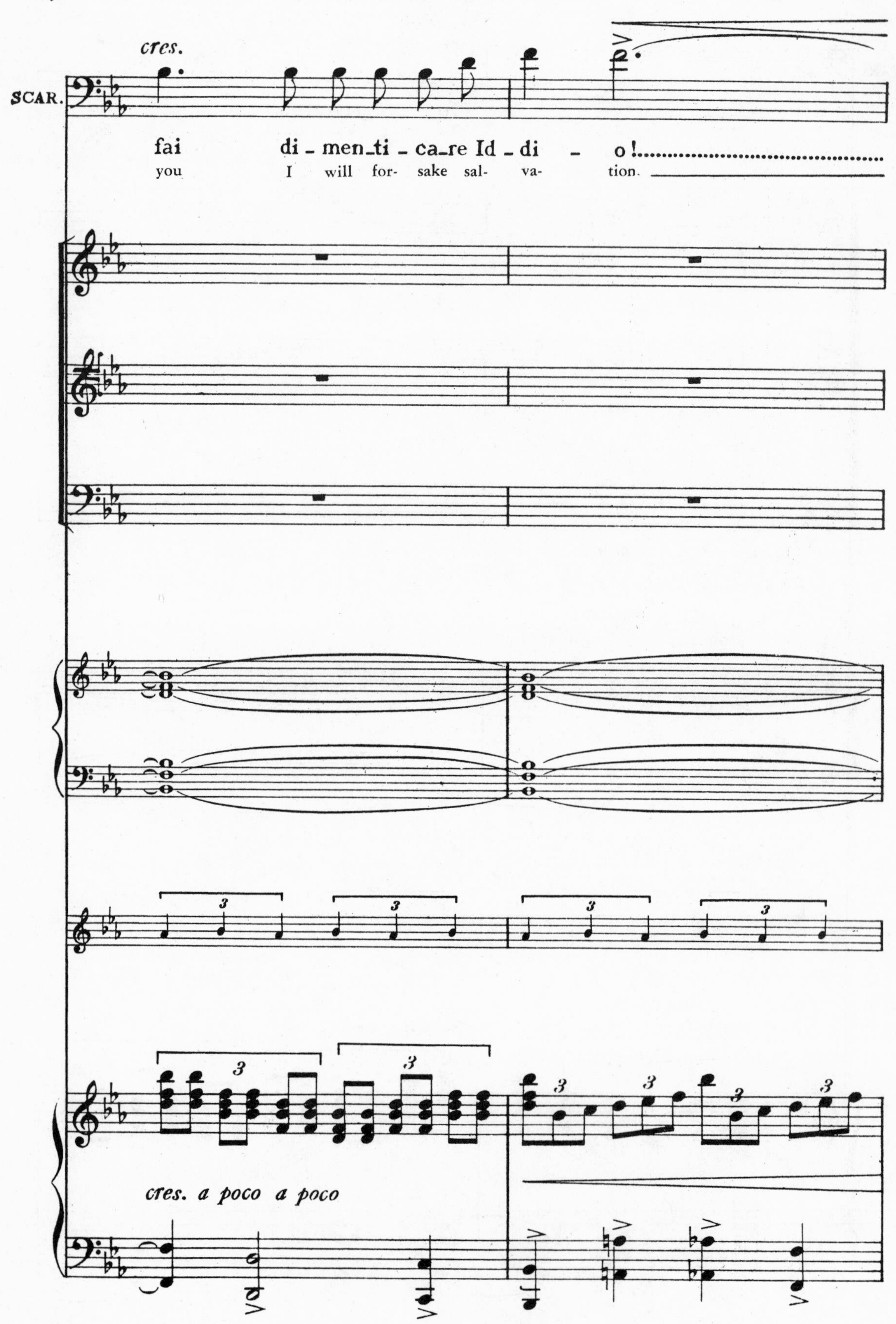
cres.
SCAR.
fai di - men - ti - ca - re Id - di - o!
you I will for- sake sal- va- tion.
3
cres. a poco a poco

allargando
(With religious zeal.)
GRANDIOSO
ff
SCAR.
Te ae - - ter - - num
ff
Te ae - ter - - num
ff
Te ae - - ter - num
ff
Te ae - - ter - - num
allargando
3
3
88
※ Cannone
GRANDIOSO
6
6
6
9
allargando e cres. molto
ff
(Ottoni)

AND.te MOSSO 𝅗𝅥 = 112
SCAR.
Pa _ _ trem om_nis ter_ra.... ve_ne _ ra _ _ tur!
Pa _ _ trem om_nis ter_ra.... ve_ne _ ra _ _ tur!
Pa _ _ trem om_nis ter_ra.... ve_ne _ ra _ _ tur!
Pa _ _ trem om_nis ter_ra.... ve_ne _ ra _ _ tur!
AND.te MOSSO 𝅗𝅥 = 112
89
tutta forza
ff
(The curtain falls quickly.)
8
allarg:...
fff
fff
Fine dell'Atto I.o

# ACT II

## PALAZZO FARNESE

(Scarpia's room; a large window facing the court of the palace. A table is set for supper. It is night.)

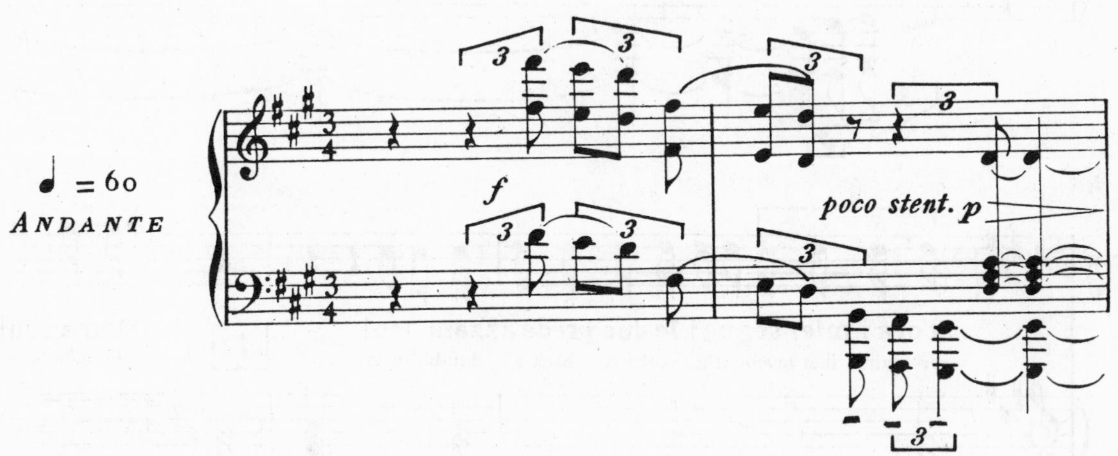


(Scarpia sits at the table and dines; occasionally interrupting his meal to ponder.

He takes out his watch; his nervous attitude betrays a feverish anxiety.)

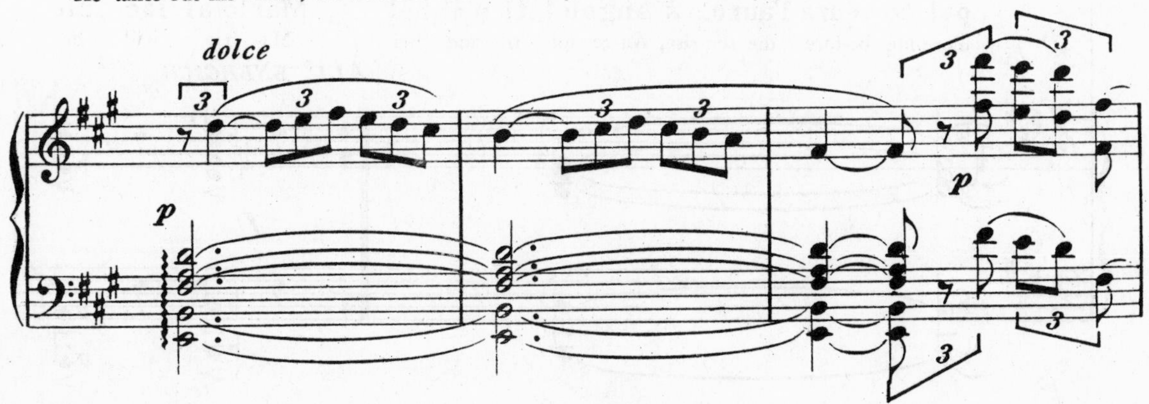

SCARPIA
poco stent.
Tosca è un buon falco!..
To - sca's my fal-con,
Certo a que_
And I am
poco stent.
pp
CAR.
_st'ora i miei segugi le due prede azzannano!
cer- tain that my hunters will bring back a dou-ble prey.
1
Doman sul
To-mor- row
pp
ALL.° ENERGICO
SCAR.
pal_co vedrà l'auro_ra Angelot_ti e il bel
morn-ing, be-fore the sun-rise, An-ge- lot- ti and her
Mario al lac_cio
Ma- rio will be
ALL.° ENERGICO
f

1º Tempo
(He rings.)
SCAR.
pen_dere.
hang-ing high!
1º Tempo
poco stentando
ff
(dopo la parola)
p
pp
(Sciarrone enters.)
SCAR.
Tosca è a pa_lazzo?..
To-sca is not here yet?
a piacere
SCIARRONE
Un ciambellan ne uscia pur ora in
One of your of-fi-cers has gone to
col canto
Mosso
SCI
2
trac_cia...
fetch her.
Mosso
a tempo

(To Sciarrone, pointing to the window.)

SCARPIA I.º TEMPO
poco stent.
Apri.
O-pen!
I.º TEMPO
poco stent.
p

(The sound of an orchestra is heard from a lower floor, where the Queen is giving a brilliant party in

TEMPO DI GAVOTTA MOLTO MOD.to
SCAR.
Tarda è la notte...
Night is ad- vanc-ing,
3
TEMPO DI GAVOTTA MOLTO MOD.to
p

honor of Melas.)

(To himself.)
poco rall.
a tempo
poco rall.
SCAR.
p
Alla can_tata ancor manca la Diva,
but the Can- ta- ta cannot start with-out To-sca.
poco rall.
a tempo
poco rall.

(To Sciarrone.)
a tempo
SCAR.
e strimpellan ga_votte.
_They are scratching their fiddles.
Tu attenderai la Tosca in sull'en_
Go down and wait for To- sca at the
a tempo
4
SCAR.
_trata;
en-trance.
le dirai ch'io l'aspetto finita la can_ta_ta...
Tell her I want to see her as soon as she has fin-ished,
pp
(Sciarrone is about to leave.)
(Scarpia rises, goes to his desk, and hastily
poco rit.
rall.
SCAR.
o meglio...
or bet- ter,
poco rit.
rall.
writes a note.)
a tempo
(Gives the note to Sciarrone, who then leaves.)
SCAR.
5
8
le darai questo bi_
here's a note that you will
PP a tempo
pp rall.
pp
p

ANDte LENTO
(To himself.)
(Returns to the table and pours himself
SCAR.
- glietto.
hand her.
Ella verrà...
I'm sure she'll come
ANDte LENTO
pp
a glass of wine.)
Sostenendo
SCAR.
per a-mor del suo Ma - rio!
out of love for her Ma- rio.
Sostenendo
pp
p
poco rall.
SCAR.
Per a-mor del suo
Out of love for her
poco rall.

SCAR.
affrettando
Ma_rio........ al piacer mio s'arrende - rà.
Ma- rio —— she will sur- ren- der to my will.
f
mf
affrettando
p
SCAR.
p e cupo
poco rall.
Tal dei profondi a_mo_ri è la profonda mi_seria.
There is no great-er suff'-ring than the suff'-ring that love brings.
ppp
col canto
ANDte UN PO' AGITATO = 104
SCAR.
Ha più for - te sa - po - re........... la con_quista vïo -
6
Sweet- er far are the rap- tures —— of a vi- o- lent
ANDte UN PO' AGITATO = 104
p

poco rit.
SCAR.
_len _ ta.........che il mellifluo con_sen _ so............ Io di so_
con- quest than of wil- ling sur- ren- der. A lov- er
poco rit.
a tempo
deciso
SCAR.
_spi _ ri e di lat_ti_gi _ no_se albe lu_na _ ri po_co m'ap_
sigh- ing and pin-ing in the splen- dor of the moon- light is- n't my
a tempo
p
f
SCAR.
_pa _ go....... Non so trar _ re ac_cordi di chi _ tarra, nè oròscopo di
fash - ion! Not for me the po- et- ry of sun-sets, of mid-night se-re-
p
sf
p

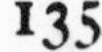

*sostenendo molto*

(With disdain.)

SCAR.

*p*

fior,......................... nè far l'occhio di
nades. —— I nev- er ask a

*mf*

*pp sostenendo molto*

*dim.* *pp rit.* *cres.*

SCAR.

pe - sce,......... o tubar come tor - tora!
flow- er: —— "Does she love me or love me not?"

7

*dim. e rall.*

*cres.* *string.*

(Rises but stays close to the table.)

SCAR.

*f*

ANDte MODto
SCAR.
Bra - mo. La cosa bramata per - seguo, me ne sazio e via la
Al- ways I crave for the things that e- lude me. Once I've had them I can dis-
ANDte MODto
ff
f
getto... volto a nuo- va e - sca.
card them. On to strong-er pleas-ures.
8
Dio cre - ò.........
God cre- a- -
ff
f
....... diverse bel - tà, vini di - versi...
- - ted more than one wine, more than one beau-ty.
Io vo' gu -
I want to
ff

cres. ed allargando
SCAR.
_star quanto più posso dell'o _ pra di _ vi_na!
taste all I can wring from the Hand of the Mak-er.
ff
cres. ed allargando
ff strepitoso
(Very excited, yells.)
(Sits down.)
SCAR.
Entri. In buon punto.
Splen-did. Send him in here.
SCIARR.
(Enters.)
(Leaves to call Spoletta,
Spoletta è giunto.
Spo-let-ta's wait-ing.
9
cres. e string.
pesante e stentato
dim.
who returns with him; Sciarrone remains at the door.)
ff rapidamente

SPOLETTA
ALL? MOD!o
(Comes closer, frightened.)
(To himself.)
(Sant' I_gnazio m'a_
(Saint Ig- na- tius as-
(Sitting down, he continues his meal while interrogating Spoletta without looking at him.)
SCARPIA
O galan_tuomo, com'andò la caccia?..
Home is the hunt-er. And where is the quar-ry?
ALL? MOD!o
f
meno f
p
SPOL.
_iu_ta!)
sist me!)
Della si_gnora seguimmo la trac_cia.
Just as you or-dered, we fol-lowed the la- dy
pp
SPOL.
Giun_ti a un'erma vil_let_ta tra le fratte per_du_ta...
till she ar-rived at a vil- la, tucked a-way in a pine- grove.

10
SPOL.
ella v'entrò,.....
First, she went in,
N'esci sola ben pre_sto.
but re-turned in a mo- ment.
LO STESSO MOV.to
brillante
SPOL.
Al_lor sca_val_co lesto il muro del giardin coi miei ca_
I, with my a- gents, climbed the gar-den wall. The rest of it was
brillante
mf
SPOL.
_gnotti e piombo in ca_sa...
eas- y. And so we en- tered. . .
f
SCAR.
Quel bra_vo Spo_letta!
My good old Spo- let- ta!
6
ff secca f
ben stacc. e marcato

(Hesitates.)
SPOL.
Fiuto!.. razzo_lo!.. frugo!..
look-ing ev-e-ry-where, search-ing.
ff
f
SPOL.
3
Non s'è tro _ vato!
We could-n't find him.
(Noticing Spoletta's hesitation he gets up, pale with fury, frowning.)
SCAR.
Ahi· l'Ange _ lotti!.. Ah
And An- ge- lot- ti? Not
11
molto marcato
accel. e cres.
SCAR.
ca _ ne! Ah tradi _ to _ re! Cef _ fo di ba _ si _
find him? Try- ing to cheat me! Son of the dev- il's
accel. e cres.

(Trembling, he tries to appease Scarpia.)
SPOL.
(Shouting.)
Ge - sù!
Oh Lord!
SCAR.
-li-sco, alle forche!..
moth-er! I will hang you.
Tornando al tempo
ff
p
(Timidly.)
SPOL.
C'e - ra il pit - tor...
But he was there.
(Interrupts him.)
SCAR.
Ca-va-ra-
Ca- va- ra-
(Nods "yes" but adds:)
SPOL.
3
3
Ei sa do-ve l' altro s'a-
He knows where the oth- er one's
SCAR.
-dossi?
dos- si?
12
p

SPOL.
-scon - de...
hid- ing;
O-gni suo ge - sto
but eve- ry ges- ture,
ogni accen - to, tra-
eve- ry word that he
SPOL.
- dìa tal bef - far - da i - ro - ni - a,
spoke, was so full of de- fi-ance
ch'io lo trassi in ar-
that I had him ar-
Un poco meno
SPOL.
- re - sto...
rest- ed.
(Relieved.)
(quasi parlato)
SCAR.
Me - no ma - le!
That is bet- ter
(Paces the room; suddenly he stops: through the open window
13
Un poco meno
sensibile
p
senza rall.

Sop. 1i
AND.te SOST.to
Sa - le, a - scende l'uman can - ti
Ever higher human voices
Sop. 2i
Sa - le, a - scen_de l'u_man can - ti
Ever higher human voices
Contr.
CORO INTERNO
Sa - le, a - scen_de l'u_man can - ti
Ever higher human voices
(Guida Coro)
p legato
one hears the Cantata performed in honor of the Queen. This means Tosca has arrived.)
(Pointing to the ante-room.)
SPOL.
Egli è là.
He's outside.
sempre P e staccato
_co var - ca - spa - zi,
soar through the eons
_co var - ca spa - zi,
soar through the eons
_co var - ca spa - zi,
soar through the eons
(Suddenly struck by an idea, he says to Spoletta, who leaves:)
SCAR.
(To Sciarrone.)
Intro_du_cete il Cava_lier.
Go bring the gentleman in here.
A me Ro_ber_ti e il
I want Roberti, and

var - - ca cè - li
up to heav - en,
var - - ca cè - li
up to heav - en,
var - - ca cè - li per i - -
up to heav - en, to the
(Sitting at the table again.)
(Spoletta, and three agents, bring
SCAR.
Giudi_ce del Fi_sco.
ask the judge to see me.
14
p sensibile
per i _ gno _ ti em _ pi - re _ i,
to the Lord's e - ter - ni - ty,
per i - - gno - ti so _ li em _ pi - re _ i,
ris - ing to the Lord's e - ter - ni - ty,
_gno - - ti so - - li em - pi - re _ i,
re - gions of e - ter - ni - ty,
in Cavaradossi; followed by Roberti, the torturer, a judge, a clerk, and Sciarrone.)
CAVARADOSSI
(Rushing in, in great anger.)
Tal vio_
What an
senza rall.
f

pro - fe - ta - ti dai Van - ge -
as the gos - pel had fore - told

pro - fe - ta - ti dai Van - ge -
as the gos pel had fore - told

pro - fe - ta - ti dai Van -
as the gos pel had for

*deciso con forza*

CAV. -len-za!.. Vo' sa-
What's all

SCAR. out-rage! (With studious courtesy.)

Cava-lier, vi piaccia accomo-darvi...
Please sit down. I'm ver - y glad to see you.

*f*

*poco rall:* ........................ *a tempo*

-li, a te giun - ge o re de-i re!
us, reach - ing Him Who is King of Kings.

-li, a te giun - ge o re dei re!
us, reach - ing Him Who is King of Kings.

-ge-li, a te giun - ge o re dei re!
told us, reach - ing Him Who is King of Kings.

*poco rall.* ........................

(Declining.) *poco rall.* *a tempo*

CAV. -per... A - spetto
this? I'm waiting.

**15**

(Indicating a seat opposite him at the table.) (Staring at Cavaradossi

SCAR. Se-de-te... E sia!
Be seat - ed. All right.

*poco rall.*

*p*

*p*

(Off-stage.)
TOSCA
A te
The Lord!
Sop. 1.i
A
To
Sop. 2.i
A
To
Contr.
A
To
Ten.
vo - li a te.
Praise the Lord,
Bassi
Que - sto can - to vo - li a te.
All our sing - ing is for the Lord.
before interrogating him.)
SCAR
V'è noto che un pri -
You must have heard the
senza rall.

T
que _ st'inno di gloria vo_li a te..........
We sing for the high-er glory of the Lord.
te.......... que _ st'in _ no vo _ li or
Him our sing - ing ris - es, the
te.......... que _ st'in _ no vo _ li som _ mo Iddio del _ ia vit _
Him our sing - ing ris - es, Lord for - ev - er great and
te.......... que _ st'in _ no vo _ li som _ mo Id _
Him our sing - ing ris es, Lord, great and
Dio che
He was
(Hearing Tosca's voice he exclaims, emotionally:)
CAVAR.
La sua voce!..
That is To-sca!
(Hearing Tosca's voice he interrupts himself.)
(Continues his questioning.)
SCAR.
_gione,.. v'è no _ to che un pri _
sto - ry — — the sto - ry of the

T.
Or vo
We sing
vo li a te!
glo ry of the Lord.
Som mo Id
To-geth- er
to ria
might y.
Que st'in
This hymn
di o
might y.
Que
E-
Que st'in no a te!
for Him we sing.
fo sti in nanzi ai se co li,
Lord be fore the world be- gan,
CAV.
I
I
SCAR.
gio ne oggi è fug gi to da Ca stel San t' angelo?
man who bolt - ed this morn-ing from Cas- tel Sant' An- ge-lo.
16

T.
li quest'u man in no di glo
our fervent song of high - er glo
di o al le
with the an gels
no di glo ria
we are sing ing.
st'in no a te
ter nal glo ry!
al le can ti che de
long be fore the an gels
CAV.
gno ro.
have not.
SCAR.
Ep pur si pre ten de che vo i l' abbiate ac
And yet I am told that you saw him this very

p cres.
T.
ria a tel
ry to Him,
f
can ti che de glian
we will raise our voic
al le can ti che de glian ge
joins the ho ly an gels' lov ing
Som mo Id dio del la vit to
Lord Who Al might y thrones in heav
heav
gli an ge li que. st'in
sang their songs. This hymn
(With determination.)
CAV.
Men_zogna!
They're ly_ing.
SCAR.
colto in Sant'Andrea, prov_vi_sto di ci_bo e di vesti...
day in Sant' An- drea; sup- plied him with food and with cloth-ing,
cres.

T
ge - li, que - st'in - - no vo - li a te!
es high to sing the glory of the Lord.
li s'u - ni - - sca e vo - li a te!
throng, to sing the glory of the Lord,
ria, or vo - - li a te! Que - -
en, we sing of Him. This
ria! Que - st'in - - no a te!
en, of Him we sing,
no di glo - - - - ria, or
of His glo - - - - ry we
CAV.
Nego. Le
Nonsense! Who
(Remaining calm.)
SCAR.
...e gui - dato ad un vostro po - dere subur - ba - no...
and al- lowed him to hide in your vil-la in the sub- urbs.

T
A te que
The Lord, we
Que - st'in - no di glo ria. a
A hymn of His glo - ry to
Som - mo Id - dio!
King of all Kings.
Que - st'in - no di
We sing a hymn of
st'in - no di glo - ria, que - st'in - no di
hymn of His glo - ry, this hymn of His
A
of
vo - li a te, or vo - li a
sing for Him. This hymn we sing to
CAV.
prove?
says so?
(Anxiously.)
Al fatto.
That's nonsense.
Chi m'ac-cusa?
Who ac-cused me?
SCAR.
Un suddito fe-dele....
A very faithful servant.

p rall.
a tempo
T
st'in no di glo ria!
sing for His glo ry.
te, a te!
Him, to Him.
glo ria! a te!
glo ry to Him.
glo ria! vo li a te!
glo ry. We sing to Him.
te, a te!
Him we sing.
te, a te!
Him, to Him.
pp rall: a tempo
(With irony.)
rall: a tempo
CAV.
I vostri birri invan fru-gâr la villa.
Your agents searched but found my vil-la emp-ty.
SCAR.
17
Segno che è bence-
That on-ly proves you're
sensibile
p rall:
p a tempo

T
Sa - le, a - - scende l'u - man
Ev - er high-er hu - man
Sa - le, a - - scende l'u - man
Ev - er high-er hu - man
Sa - le, a - - scende l'u - man
Ev - er high-er hu - man
Sa - le, a - - scende l'u - man
Ev - er high-er hu - man
Sa - le, a - - scende l'u - man
Ev - er high-er hu - man
A - - - scen - de l'u - man
High - - er and high er
CAV.
SPOL.
So_spetti di spia!
All spies are sus- pi-cious.
(Breaks in, offended.)
Al_le no_stre ri-
Eve-ry ques- tion we
SCAR.
_lato.
clev-er.
senza rall.
pp

T.
can - - - ti - - co
voic - - - es soar
can - - - ti - - co
voic - - - es soar
can - - - ti - - co
voic - - - es soar
p
can - - - ti - - co var - - -
voic - - - es soar through
(Falsetto)
can - - - ti - - co var - - -
voic - - - es soar through
can - - - ti - - co
voic - - - es soar.
p
CAV.
E ri_do an_cor.
And still I laugh,
SPOL
_cer_che e_gli ri_de_va...
asked he an-swered with laugh-ter.

T.
var - - - - - ca
through the
spa - - - - - zi
e - - - - - ons
var - - - - - ca
through the
spa - - - - - zi
e - - - - - ons
var - - - - - ca
through the
spa - - - - - zi
e - - - - - ons
- - - - - ca
the
spa - - - - - zi
e - - - - - ons
- - - - - - ca
the
spa - - - - - zi
e - - - - - ons
CAV.
e ri - do an - cor.
and still I laugh.
SCARPIA
(Terrifying, in his anger.)
Que - sto è luo - go di
I think tears more ap-

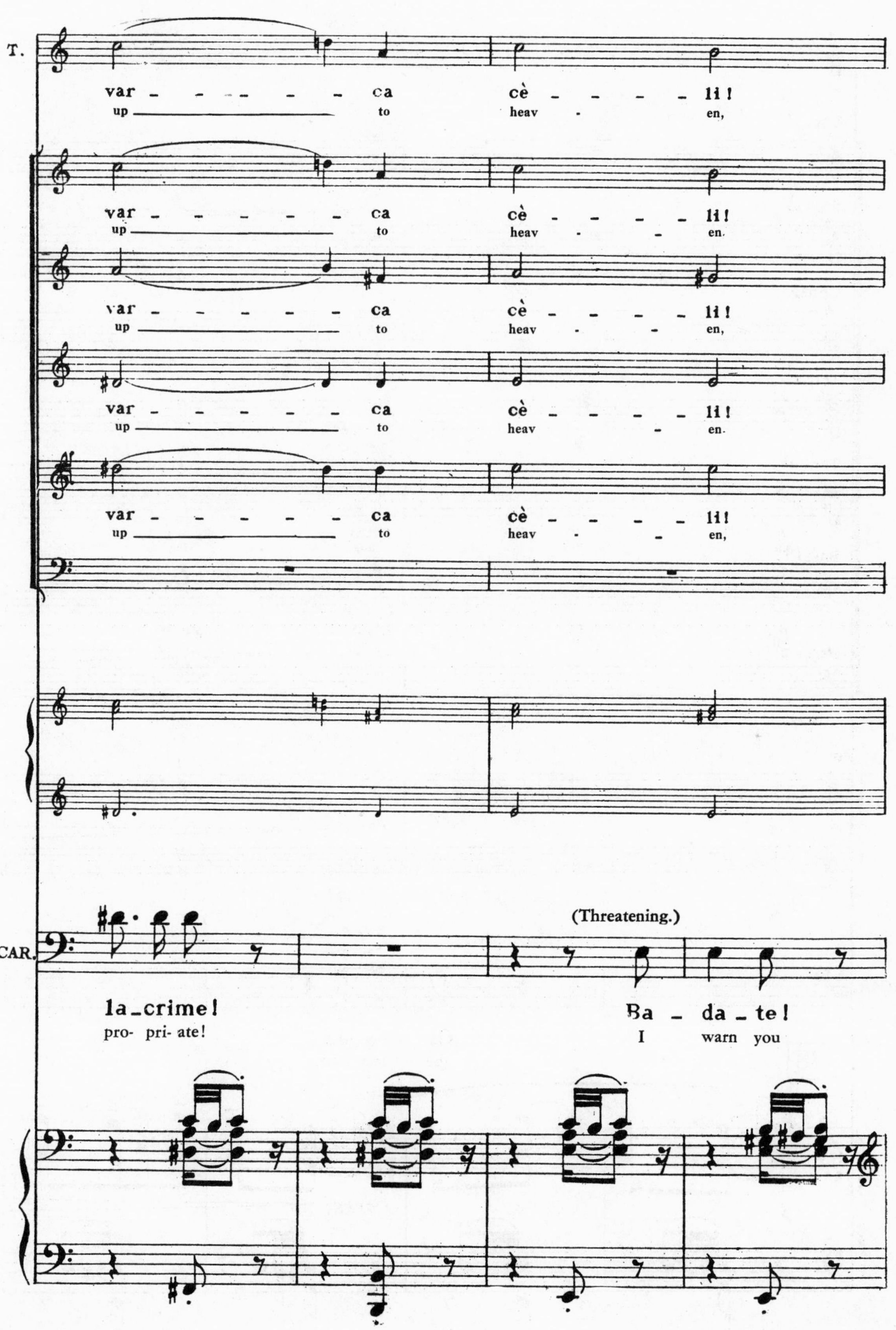
T.
var - ca cè - li!
up to heav - en,
var - ca cè - li!
up to heav - en.
var - ca cè - li!
up to heav - en,
var - ca cè - li!
up to heav - en.
var - ca cè - li!
up to heav - en,
SCAR.
la_crime!
pro- pri- ate!
(Threatening.)
Ba - da - te!
I warn you

T.
Sop. 1i
Sop. 2i
cres.
A
to
Contr.
A
Let
te
us
Ten. 1i
A
t'o
te
Him,
o
the
Ten. 2i
cres.
A
All
te
our
giun
sing
ge o
ing
Bassi 1.
A
All
te
our
giun
sing
ge o
ing
Bassi 2.
cres.
cres.
(Nervously.)
cres.
SCAR.
Or
the
ba_sta!
last time.
18
p
cres.

poco allarg: ...........
T.
ff
A te o re dei
to Him, the King of
A .................... te o re dei
to Him, the King of
te .................... giun - - geo re dei
Him Who is King of
giun - - ge a te o re dei
sing to Him, the King of
re dei re, o re dei
King of Kings, the King of
re dei re, o re dei
is for Him, the King of
re dei re, o re dei
is for Him, the King of
o re dei
The King of
(Irritated and disturbed by the voices of the Cantata, he closes the window.)
SCAR.
Ri - spon - de - te!
You will an - swer.
f
poco allarg: ...........

a tempo
T.
re!
Kings.
re!
Kings.
re!
Kings.
re!
Kings.
re!
Kings.
re!
Kings.
re!
Kings.
re!
Kings.
CAVAR.
f
Non lo
I don't
(Imperiously.)
ff
SCAR.
Ov'è An_ge _ lot_ti?
Where's An- ge - lot ti?
19
a tempo
5
f
ff

CAV.
SCAR.
so.
know.
Ne - ga - te d'a-ver-gli da-to ci - bo?
I ask, is it true that you have fed him?
ff
Ne-go!
Nev- er.
Ne-go!
Nev- er.
E ve-sti?
Dis-guised him?
E a-si-lo nel-la villa? E che là sia na-scosto?
Re-ceived him in your vil- la, where right now he's hid-ing?
(Emphatically.)
Ne-go! ne-go!
Nev- er, nev- er.
UN POCO MENO
20
deciso
subito P

(Remaining calm, almost paternal.)
SCAR.
Via, Ca_va_lie_re, ri_flet_te_te: sag_gia non è co_
May I sug- gest you think it o- ver? Noth- ing is to be
pp
_testa o_sti_na_tez_za vo_stra. An_goscia grande, pronta confes_
gained by your re- main- ing stub- born. You will re- gret it if you don't con-
poco allarg:
allarg.
_sione e_vi_te_rà! Io vi consiglio,
fess your e- vil deeds. Let me ad-vise you:
molto espressivo, lamentoso
rit:

lentamente
Come prima
SCAR.
di_te:
speak up!
do_v'è dunque Ange_lot_ti?
Tell me, where's An- gel- lot- ti?
21
ff
lentamente
Come prima
CAVAR.
Non lo so.
I don't know.
SCAR.
f
An_cor, l'ul_ti_ma vol_ta. Dov'è?
I ask you for the last time where is he?
CAV.
Nol so!
Don't know.
SPOL.
(O bei tratti di
He is ask-ing for
deciso
ff
dim.

ANDANTE
(Tosca enters, alarmed: seeing Cavaradossi, she runs towards him and embraces him.)
SPOL
cor - da!)
SCARPIA trou- ble.
(Ec - - co - la!)
Here she is.
ANDANTE
p
TOSCA
Ma-rio, tu qui?!
CAVAR. Ma-rio, you here?
(Whispers to Tosca, who indicates that she understands.)
(Di quan-to là ve-de-sti,
Don't say a word of what you
CAV.
ta-ci. o m'uccidi!)
SCARPIA saw there, if you love me.
MOLTO SOSTENUTO
con forza e sost.
Mario Cavara-dos-si, qual testi-
Ma-rio Ca-va-ra-dos-si, this wor-thy
ff col canto
ff
pesante e sost.

22

*cres.*

(Motions to Sciarrone to open the door to the torture chamber.)

SCAR.

-mone il Giudi-ce v'a-spetta.
judge will take your dep- o- si- tion.

*marcatissimo e sost.*

*cres. molto* *ff*

(Turning to Roberti.)

*a piacere*

SCAR.

Pria le forme ordi-na-rie... Indi... ai miei
Try the u- sual pro- ce- dure. Lat-er I'll in-

*col canto* ..................................

*m.d.*

*Lento*

(The judge enters the torture chamber: the others follow him,

LENTO

SCAR.

cenni...
struct you

23

LENTO

*ppp*

*rall.* *pp*

leaving Tosca and Scarpia behind; Spoletta withdraws to the door at the back of the room.)

*cres.* *f* *p* *p* *cres.*

*passionale*

24

(Sciarrone closes the door. Tosca shows surprise; Scarpia reassures her, being elaborately gentle with her.)

*p* *pp* *sost.*

*pp*

*affrett.* *pp rit.*

SCARPIA

AND.no MOD.to ♩. = 58

(With gallantry.) *p*

Ed
Now

25

AND.no MOD.to ♩. = 58

*rall:*

*p*

(Asking Tosca to sit down.)

SCAR.

or fra noi par_liam da buoni a_mi_ci. Via quel_

you and I can have a word in friend-ship. No more

TOSCA
(Sits down, pretending calm.)
Sgo - mento alcun non ho...
I don't know what you mean.
SCAR.
-l'a - ria sgo-men-ta - ta...
sor- row on that love- ly face?
(With simulated indifference.)
T.
(Passes behind the sofa where Tosca sits and leans against it.)
Fu sciocca gelo-si-a...
I'm not a jeal-ous wom-an.
La sto-ria del ven-taglio?..
The fan that we dis- covered—
p
poco rit
No:
No.
L'Atta - van-ti non e-ra dunque alla vil-la?
Do you mean that you did- n't find L'At- ta- van- ti?
poco rit

a tempo
T.
e_gli e_ra so_lo.
No one was with him.
(Inquiring maliciously.)
SCAR.
So_lo?
Real-ly?
Ne sie_te ben si_
How can you be so
a tempo
26
fm.s.
p
pp
(Annoyed, insistingly.)
T.
Nulla sfugge ai gelo_si.
Jeal-ous eyes are the sharp-est.
So_lo! so_lo!
There was no one.
(Puts a chair in front of Tosca; staring at her he sits down.)
SCAR.
_cu_ra?
cer- tain?
(Irritated.)
T.
So_lo! sì!
No one, no!
SCAR.
f
p
Davver?!
In-deed!
Quanto fuo_co!
What an out- burst!
Par che abbia_te pa_
One could al- most be-
27
f
p

(Turning towards the door of the torture chamber, he shouts:)

SCAR.

-u-ra di tra-dir-vi. Sciarro-ne: che dice il Cava-lier?
lieve that you were fright-ened. Sciar-ro- ne, what does our wit-ness say?

TOSCA

(Laughing.)

Oh! è i-nu-til!
Oh, it's use- less.

(Louder.)

SCAR.

In-si-stia-mo.
Let's con- tin- ue.

SCIARR. (Appearing at the door.)

(Sciarrone goes back, closing the door.)

Ne-ga.
Noth-ing.

*f*

*cres.*

(Slowly, with an ironic smile.)

*rit.*

T.

(Rises, paces about the room; seriously.)

Dunque per compia-cervi, si dovrebbe men-
May- be you'd like it bet-ter if I told you a

SCAR.

Lo vedremo, si-gno ra.
We shall find out, Si- gno- ra.

*ff*

*pp* *rall. col canto*

ANDte SOSTENUTO ♩. = 42

T.
_tir?
lie?

SCAR.
No: ma il ve_ro po_trebbe abbre_viargli u_n'o_ra as_sai pe_
No, but tel_ling the truth might a_void some most un_pleas_ant

28

*p legato e cres.*

(Astonished.)

T.
Un'o_ra pe_no_sa? Che vuol dir?......... Che avviene in quella
Some un_pleas_ant mo_ments? In what way? What's hap_pen_ing to

SCAR.
_no_sa...
mo_ments.

*p* *f*

*rall:* ......................... *a tempo* *cres. molto*

T.
stanza?
Ma_rio?
Oh! Dio!... che av_
Oh God, what

*rall:*

SCAR.
*f*
È forza che s'adempia la leg_ge.
There is a law and I shall en_force it.

29

*p* *col canto* ......................

*f con forza, martellate cres. molto*

T.
_vien,
che avvien,
che av_vien?!!.........
law?
Go on,
Go on!
(With increased vehemence.)
SCAR.
Le_ga_to mani e piè il vostro a_
They've tied him hand and foot, and they have
pp
dim.
SCAR.
_man_te ha un cerchio un_ci_na_to al_le
laid a steel-point-ed ring o-ver his
dim
f
f deciso
SCAR.
tempia, che ad ogni nie_go ne spriz_za san_gue sen_za mer_
tem-ples. For eve-ry ques-tion he does not an-swer he pays in
f deciso

TOSCA
(Jumping up.)
Non è ver, non è ver!.................................. Sog - ghigno di
Oh no, oh no. Con - tempt-i- ble
SCAR.
-cè!
blood.
8
ff
(She listens in great anxiety, her hands clutching the back of the sofa.)
T.
30
demone.......
tor- tur-er!
pp
3
CAVAR.
(A long moan.)
Ahi-
Ah.-
espressivo molto rall:...........
p

affrettando
TOSCA (quasi parlato)
Un ge_mi_to? Pie_tà,....... pie_tà!.......
How hor- ri- ble! E- nough,— e- nough.—
CAV.
_mè!......................
p
affrettando
T
Eb_ben....... ma cessa_te,cessa_te!
All right, but re-lease him, re-lease him!
SCARPIA
Sta in voi sal_var_lo.
It's your de- ci- sion.
p
cres.
(Opens the door to the torture chamber.)
SCAR.
Sciar_ro_ne, scio_glie_te.
Sciar- ro- ne, e- nough now.
poco allarg.
f
ff

SCAR.
Tut_to.
Stop it!
(Appearing at the door.)
SCIARR.
(Returning to the torture chamber, he closes the door.)
Tut_to?
Stop it?
p
p
TOSCA
Ch'io lo ve_da!...
Let me see him.
SCAR.
31
Sostenuto molto
Ed or la ve_ri_tà...
I want to hear the truth.
No!
No.
p
dolce
p
(Has succeeded in getting close to the door.)
T.
f
pp
ppp

T.
CAVAR. (In the torture chamber.)
Ma_rio!
Ma- rio. (In pain.)
To_sca!
To- sca!
pp
rall.
3
Ti straziano anco_ra?
They still make you suf- fer?
CAV.
poco affrett.
No- co_rag_gio-
No, it's noth- ing.
col canto
poco affrett.
rit.
rall.
4
Ta_ci, ta_ci!
Courage, cour- age!
Sprezzo il do_lor!
I laugh at pain.
stentando
rall. col canto

TOSCA
LENTO GRAVE ♩=56
(With conviction.)
Non so
I know
SCARPIA
(Walking towards Tosca.)
Or_sù, To_sca, par_la_te.
And now, To - sca, I'm wait - ing.
32
LENTO GRAVE ♩=56
T.
nul_la!
noth - ing.
SCAR.
Non va_le quel_la
You don't be- lieve I
pp
f
(Standing between the door and Scarpia; trying to prevent him from giving his order.)
Più mosso
No! fer_ma_te!
No! I beg you!
(Trying to go to the door.)
pro_va?....... Roberti, ri_pi_glia_mo.......
mean it? Ro-ber- ti, let's con- tin- ue.
Voi par_le_
All right. I'm
Più mosso
ff

ALL.º MOD.to

T. No! no!...... Ah!........ mo stro.................... lo............
No, no. You're a mon - ster. How you

SCAR. -re-te?
wait-ing.

33

ALL.º MOD.to

p

T. stra - zi, ah! mo stro, lo stra - zi, l'uc-
hate him! You mon- ster, you hate him, you'll

f rit.

rit.

T. -ci - di............ ah!........ l'uc-ci - di!
SCARPIA kill him! Ah, you'll kill him!

Lo
Oh

rit.

rit.
SCAR.
stra_zia quel vo_stro si_len_zio......... as_sai
no, it's not Scar_pia who'll kill him! It's your
rit.
TOSCA
stringendo
Tu ri_di............ all'or_ri_da
You're laugh_ing? You laugh at his
(Laughs)
più.........
si_lence!
stringendo
T.
pe_na? (Admiringly.)
suff'ring.
Mai To_sca al_la sce_na più tra_gi_ca fu!
You've nev_er yet played a more trag_i_cal role.
34
f

(Tosca, terrified, walks away from Scarpia who, in a sudden outburst of ferocity, turns to Spoletta.)

p cres. ed accel.
(Shouting.)
SCARPIA
A - pri - te le por - te che n'o - da i la-
Let's o - pen the doors so we'll hear how he's
ff
CAVAR. (In the torture chamber.)
Mosso, vibratissimo
f
Vi sfi - - do!........
I de - fy you
(Spoletta opens the door and remains standing there.)
SCAR.
-men-ti!
scream-ing.
Mosso, vibratissimo
fff

I.º TEMPO

CAV.

Vi sfi_do!
de- fy you.

(Shouting to Roberti.)

(To Tosca.)

SCAR.

Più for_te! più for_te! Par_
Still hard- er, still hard -er. Now

35

I.º TEMPO

*p*

3

T.
Ah! non so
Ah, I know
SCAR.
vi - a
is he?
cres. poco a poco ed incalzando
5
(Desperately.)
T.
nul - la! ah!...................... do - vrei men - tir?
noth - ing. Ah, what can I do?
SCAR.
5
6

T.
(Insists.)
SCAR.
Di _ te do_v'è An_ge_ _lot_ti?
Speak, where is An- ge- lot- ti?
cres. ed incalzando ancora
5
5
T.
No! no!
No, no!
SCAR.
Di _ te do_v'è An_ge _ lot _ ti? par _
Speak, where is An- ge- lot - ti? That's
sempre cres.
5
6

allargando
T.
ah,
ah,
ah,..........
ah,
SCAR.
-la - te su,
all I ask.
vi - a, do-ve ce-la-to
Tell me where did he go to
allargando..........
6
T.
Ah! Più non pos-so!
Ah, I can't bear it.
Ah!..........che orror!...
Ah, I can-not
SCAR.
36
sta? Su, via par-
hide? It's time you
-la-te o-
told me. Speak
ff sostenendo..........

T.
Ah!......... ces - sa te il mar - tir!........... è trop - po sof -
Ah, this is too much to bear, this is too much to
SCAR.
- v'è?..........
up!
fff
rit.
rit.
T.
- frir!........... Ah! non pos - so più,........... ah! non pos - so
bear. Ah, this is too much, Ah, this is too
SCAR.
dim.
p
p

(Beseeches Scarpia, who motions to Spoletta to let Tosca approach the door: she does so, and horrified by the terrible scene, turns towards Cavaradossi.)

T.
A - scol - ta, non pos_so
I beg you. This is too
CAV.
No!
no.
calando sempre
T.
più...
much.
CAV.
Stolta, che sai?... che puoi
Tell him? You can't. You don't

CAV.
dir?...
know.
SPOL.
(Spoletta enters the chamber but soon returns. Tosca,
(Irritated by Cavaradossi's words, fearing that they might further encourage Tosca to keep silent, he yells to Spoletta.)
SCARPIA
Ma fa _ te_lo ta _ ce_re!
I want him to be si-lenced.
TOSCA
Che v'ho fat _ to in vi _ ta mia?!
Tell me why you hate me so.
Son
You
overcome with horror, falls on the sofa and turns, sobbing, to Scarpia, who remains impassible and silent.)
SPO.
calando sempre sino alla fine

T.
i _ _ o che co_sì tor_tu _ ra _ _ te!.. Tortu_ra _ te
know that it is me whom you tor- ture! In his flesh you
(Mumbling a prayer.)
SPOL.
Judex
38
pp
più piano ancora
(Bursting into wild sobs.)
rall. molto
T
l'a _ ni_ma... sì, l'a _ ni_ma mi tor_tu_
tor- ture - me. Yes, tor- ture me— tear- ing my
SPOL.
ergo cum se_de_bit quidquid latet ap_pa _ rebit Nil in_ultum re_ma_ne_bit.
pppp
col canto

(Scarpia, making the most of Tosca's despair, goes to the door and orders the torture to be continued.)

T.

-ra - - -te!
heart out!

CAVAR.

*pausa* (With a long and violent outcry.)

Ah!
(groans)

SPOL.

*Nil in-ul-tum re-ma - ne-bit!*

Ped.

(Hearing Cavaradossi's cry, Tosca suddenly rises and says to Scarpia, in a quick whisper:)

ALL°. VIVACE
T.
39
Nel pozzo... nel giar-
The well in the
ALL°. VIVACE
ff violento

(Stifling.)
T.
_di _ no...
gar- den—
Sì!..
Yes.
SCARPIA
3
Là è l'Ange _ lot _ ti?..
That's where he is . hid - ing?
p
(Shouts towards the torture chamber.)
SCAR.
Ba _ sta, Ro _ ber _ ti.
That's all, Ro - ber - ti.
dim. sempre
pp

TOSCA
(To Scarpia.)
As_sas_
Blood-y
SCIARR.
(In the door.)
È sve _ nu_to!..
He has faint-ed.
pp
T.
_si_no! Vo_glio ve _der_lo...
murd'-rer! I want to see him.
pp
(To Sciarrone.)
SCARPIA
rall.
Por_ta_te_lo qui!..
You may bring him in.
rall:

♩= 58
(Cavaradossi is brought in by the agents who put him on the sofa: he has fainted. Tosca rushes over to
AND.te SOST.to
40
P doloroso
cres.
him but is terrified to see him bleeding profusely; she covers her eyes with her hands.)
molto sost.to
f
TOSCA
(Ashamed of her weakness, she approaches Cavaradossi and covers him with her kisses and tears.)
(Sciarrone, the judge, Roberti and the clerk exit; at a sign from Scarpia, Spoletta and the agents remain.)
MENO
sostenendo
p
pp dolce
Sostenuto
(Warmly.)
T
A - mo - re...
My dar - ling—
dolcissimo
Quanto hai pe-
How you have
CAVAR.
(Coming to.)
Flo - ria!..
Flo - ria—
Sei tu?..
My love—
Sostenuto
espressivo
pp

T
_na _ _to anima mia!..
suf- _fered, Mario, my love.
Ma il giusto Iddi_o lo pu_ni
But he will an-swer be-fore the
_rà!
Lord.
No, a
No, my
CAV.
To_sca,
To_sca,
hai par_la_to?
did you tell him?
rall.
smorz.
rit.
pp
rall. molto
_mor...
love.
No!
Yes.
Dav_ve_ro?..
You're cer- tain?
(To Spoletta, with authority.)
SCARPIA
Nel poz_zo del giar_di_no-Va, Spo_
He's hid- ing in the gar-den well, Spo-

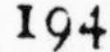

CAVAR. ALL.º VIOLENTO (Rises, threatening Tosca.)

SCAR.

-let - ta!
let - ta.

41

ALL.º VIOLENTO

ff

string:

(Falls back, broken.)

CAV.

M'hai tra - di - to!..
You've be - trayed me!

TOSCA (Embracing Cavaradossi.)

Ma - rio!
Ma - rio!

(Trying to repel her.)

CAV.

Ma - - le - det - ta!
You've be - trayed me!

f

T.
Ma - rio!
Ma - rio!
SCIAR.
(Enters in alarm.)
Ec - cel - len - za, qua - li
Ex - cel - len - cy, this is
f
p
SCARPIA
(Surprised.)
Che vuol dir quel - l'a - ria af - flit - ta?
You are trem - bling. What's the mat - ter?
SCI.
nuo - ve!..
dread - ful.
Un mes -
I have
cres.
SCAR.
Che scon - fit - ta? Co - me?
A dis - as - ter? What can
SCI.
- sag - gio di scon - fit - ta...
news of a dis - as - ter.
ff

(Shouts impatiently.)

(Cavaradossi, who has heard Sciarrone's words with increasing anxiety, finds in his returning anger the strength to get up and threatens Scarpia to his face.)

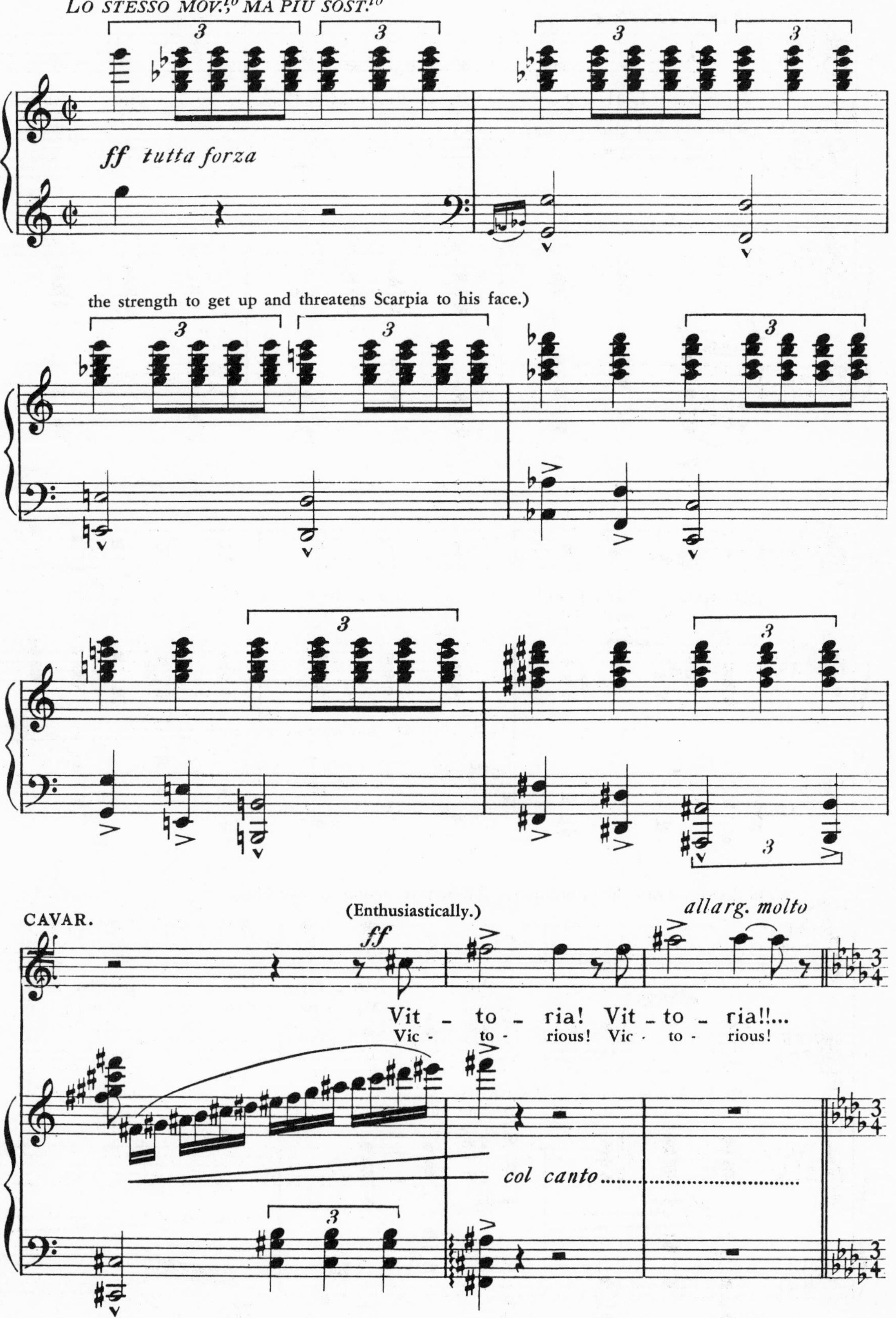
Lo stesso mov.to ma più sost.to
ff tutta forza
CAVAR.
(Enthusiastically.)
ff
allarg. molto
Vit - to - ria! Vit - to - ria!!...
Vic - to - rious! Vic - to - rious!
col canto

ALL°. CONCITATO ♩= 144
CAV.
L'al - ba vin - di - ce appar che fa
Free - dom's bu - gles call. Ty - rants
SCARPIA (With a cynical glance at Cavaradossi.)
43
ALL°. CONCITATO ♩= 144
f
f
CAV.
gli em - pi tre - mar! Li - ber - tà sor - ge,
trem - ble and fall, and u - nit - ed we cry:
f p
cres.
TOSCA (In despair, throws her arms around Cavaradossi, trying to calm him.)
Ma - rio, ta - ci, pie - tà di
allarg.
Ma - rio, Ma - rio, do think of
CAV.
crol - lan ti - ran - ni - di!
Down with all tyr - an - ny.
allarg.

T.
me!
me.
pie_
You're
CAV.
Del sof _ fer _ to mar_tir
All our an - guish and pain
me ve _
was not
SCARPIA
Bra _ veg _ gia,
I like him,
a tempo
f
p
T.
_ tà!
mad,
ta_ci!
Ma-rio!
allarg.
CAV.
_ drai qui gio_ir...
suf- fered in vain.
il tuo cor tre _ ma, o
Fear is strik - ing the breast of
SCAR.
ur_la!
rant-ing
T'affretta
and prat-ing,
a pa_le-sarmi il
it on- ly shows his
allarg:

(To Scarpia.)
f
cres.
T.
non l'a_scol _ ta _ te! Pie _ tà!........
You must not lis ten! He's mad,
CAV.
Scar _ pia, car _ ne _ fi _ ce!............ Car_
Scar - pia, the mur-der- er! You
cres.
SCAR.
fon _ do del_l'al_ma ri _ a! Va! Mo_ri _ bon _ do, il ca_
soul in its ab- ject black- ness! Go to your scaf- fold, where the
8
a tempo
cres.
(To Scarpia.)
T.
Pie _ tà!......... pie_
he's mad! For-
con forza crescente
CAV.
_ ne_fi_ce!........ Car _ ne_fi_ce!
mur- der- er! You mur-_der- er!
SCAR.
_ pe stro t'a _ spet _ ta! Va, va!
hang - mar _ is _ wait - ing. Go, go!
8

T.
_tà di me!
give him, please!
Ma _ rio... con
I go with
(Sciarrone and the agents seize Cavaradossi
CAV.
(Irritated by Cavaradossi's words, orders the agents:)
SCAR.
Por _ ta _te _me_lo via!
Re- move him from my sight!
8
cres.
(Trying to resist them.)
T.
te...
you —
No, no!
No, no!
and drag him towards the door.)
CAV.
SCAR.
Va mo_ri _ bon _ do!
Go to your scaf - fold.
Va, va!
Go, go!
string.

Largo
(Clinging to Cavaradossi, still trying to resist the agents.)
T.
Ah!
Ah,
Largo
tutta forza
fff
44
poco tratt.
poco tratt.
Ma - rio!
Ma rio,
incominciando ad affrettare un poco
Ma - rio!...
Ma - rio.
Più mosso
(Trying to pass Scarpia.)
con te,... con te!
My love, my love.
(Holding Tosca back, he closes the door.)
SCAR.
Voi no!
You stay!
Più mosso

calando
rall:

TOSCA
ANDANTE
(With a moan.)
Sal - vate_lo!
Be gen-er-ous.
SCARPIA
Io?...
I?
p
ANDANTE
p

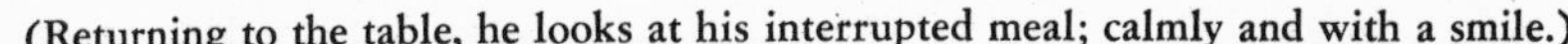
(Returning to the table, he looks at his interrupted meal; calmly and with a smile.)

SCAR.
rit.
Voi!
You!
La povera mia cena fu inter_
My mod-est lit-tle meal was in- ter-
poco stentando
p

(He sees Tosca, who stands by the door motionless and downcast.)

(Sits down, inviting Tosca to do the same.)
SCAR.
mo_do di salvar _ lo? E allor... se_de _ te...
way to save your Ma- rio? We might! Sit down here,
p
poco rit. a tempo
(He polishes a glass with his napkin and then lifts it up to the candle, inspecting it.)
SCAR.
e fa - vel - lia - mo. E intan _ to un
let's talk it o - ver. And in the
molto sostenuto
a tempo
col canto
p
dolce
p
SCAR.
sor _ so. È vin di Spa_gna...
mean - time, a glass of sher - ry.

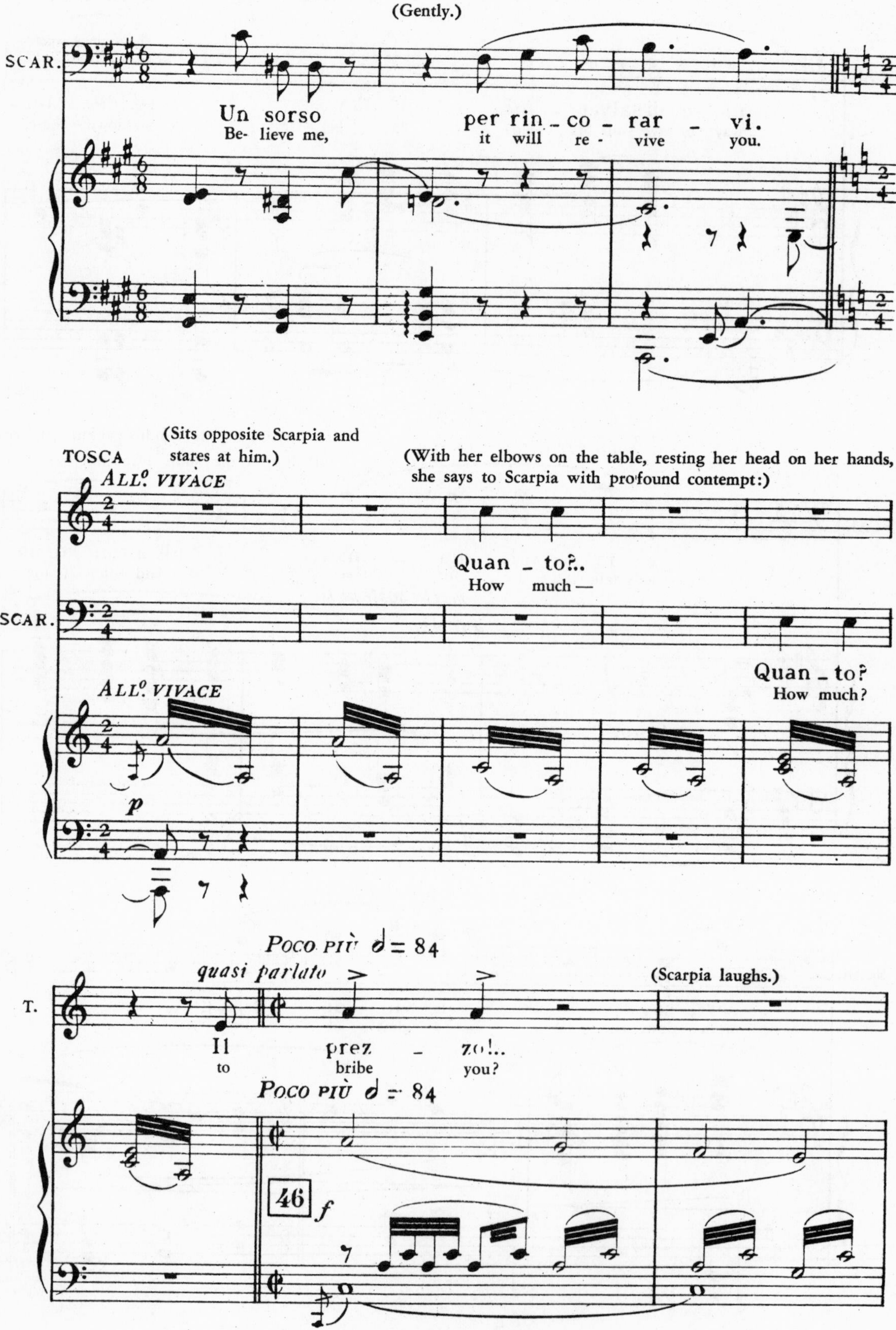
(Gently.)
SCAR.
Un sorso per rin - co - rar - vi.
Be - lieve me, it will re - vive you.
TOSCA
(Sits opposite Scarpia and stares at him.)
(With her elbows on the table, resting her head on her hands, she says to Scarpia with profound contempt:)
ALL°. VIVACE
Quan - to?..
How much—
SCAR.
Quan - to?
How much?
ALL°. VIVACE
p
POCO PIÙ 𝅗𝅥 = 84
quasi parlato
T.
Il prez - zo!..
to bribe you?
(Scarpia laughs.)
POCO PIÙ 𝅗𝅥 = 84
46
f

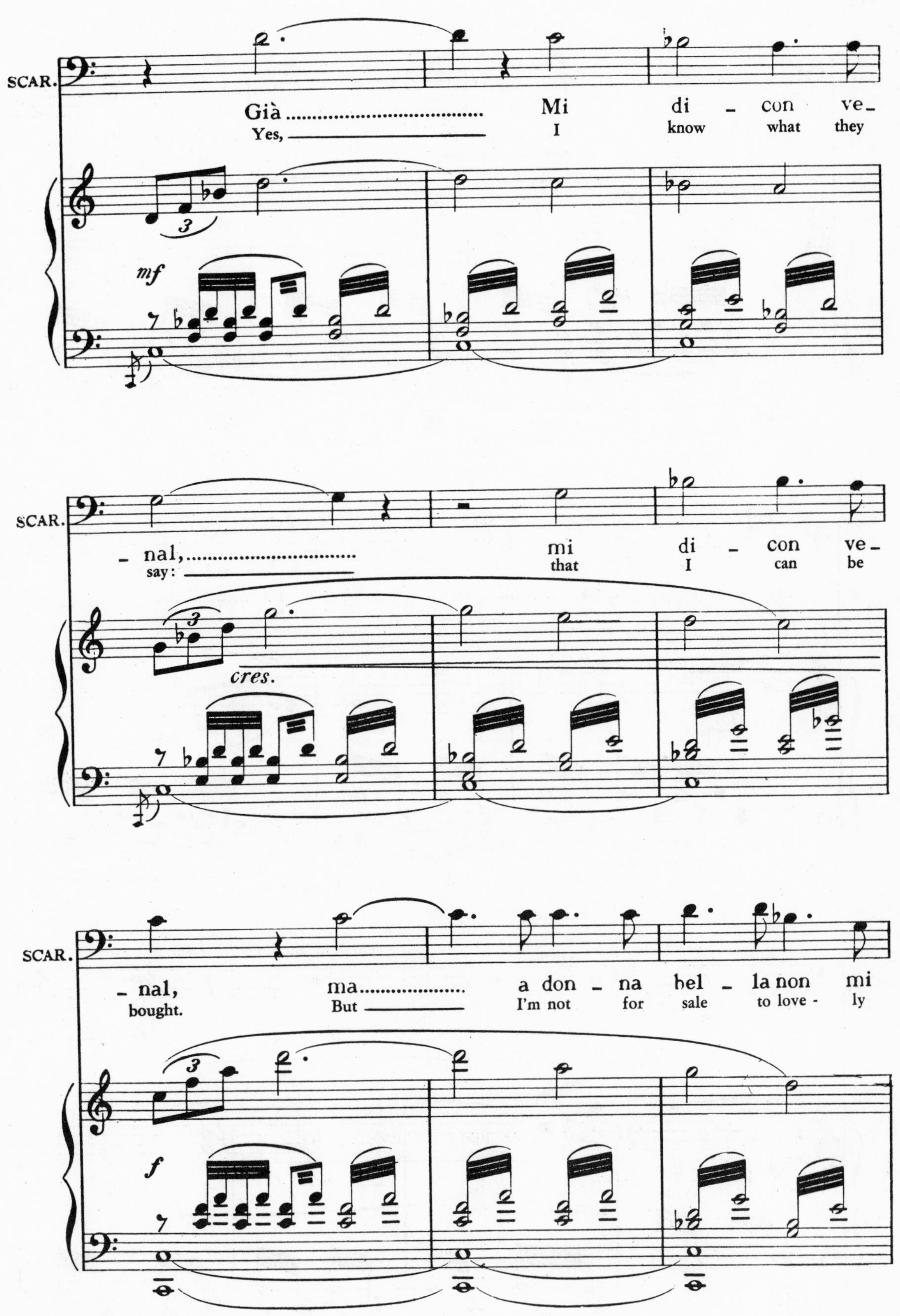
SCAR.
Già ................................ Mi di - con ve-
Yes, ________________ I know what they
mf
SCAR.
- nal, .............................. mi di - con ve-
say: ________________ that I can be
cres.
SCAR.
- nal, ma .................. a don - na bel - la non mi
bought. But ________ I'm not for sale - to love - ly
f

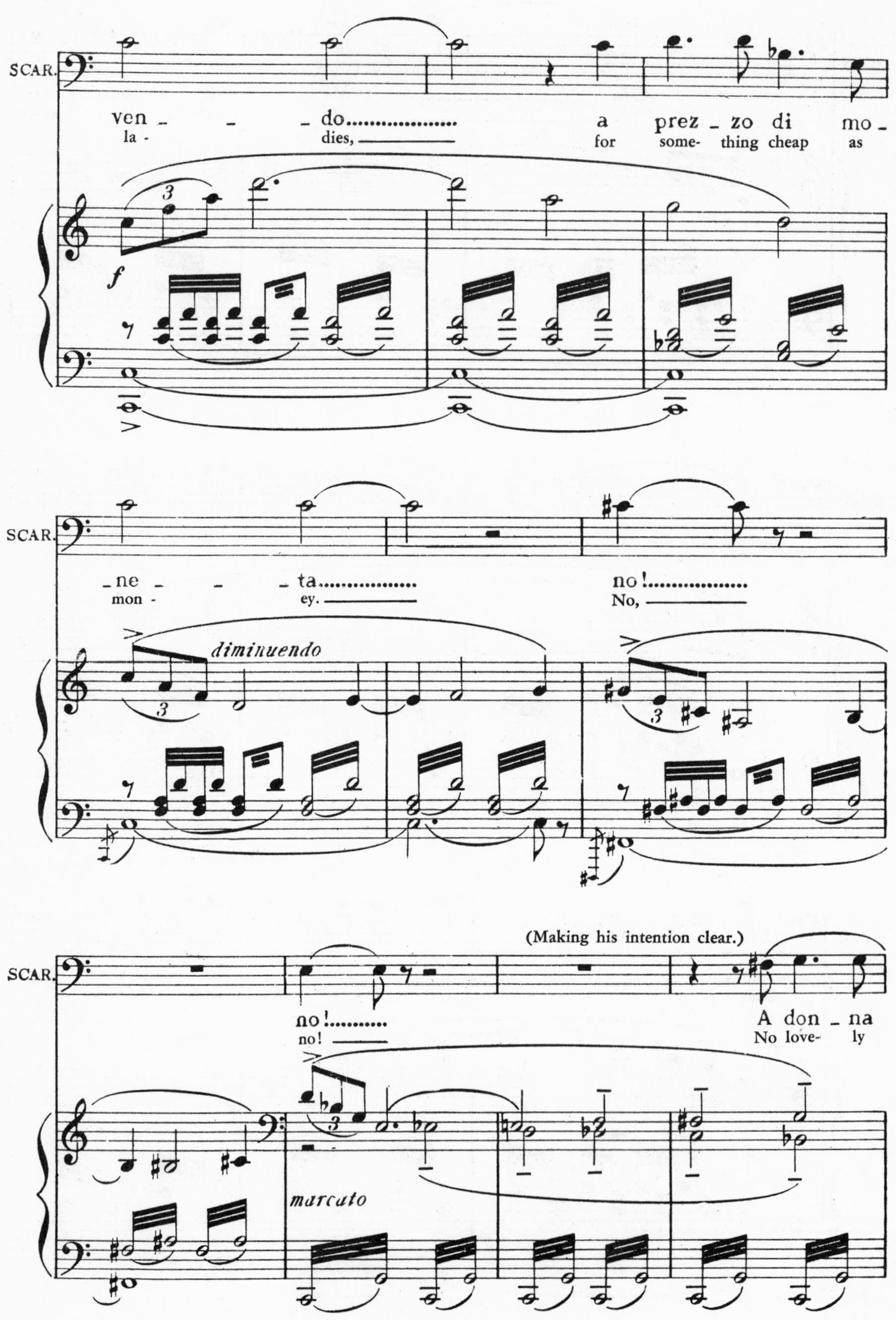
SCAR.
ven - - - do........... a prez - zo di mo -
la - dies, for some- thing cheap as
f
SCAR.
- ne - - - ta.......... no!..........
mon - ey. No,
diminuendo
(Making his intention clear.)
SCAR.
no!......... A don - na
no! No love- ly
marcato

p

SCAR.

bel - - - la io non mi ven - - - -
la dy can ev- er buy

p

SCAR.

- - do a prez_zo di mo_ne - ta.................
me with some-thing cheap as mon - ey.

p

rall. rit.

SCAR.

Se la giu_ra_ta fe_de deb_bo tra_
If I am asked to break the oath that I

47

p

*col canto* . . . . . . . . . . . . . . . . .

ANDANTE
(Very outspoken.)
SCAR.
_dir, ne voglio altra mer _ ce _ de, ne vo_glio al_tra mer_
swore, I want a high - er pay - ment; I want a much high-er
ANDANTE
p
f
molto rit.
ANDte APPASSIONATO MOLTO ♩= 69
p
_ ce _ de. Quest'o_ra io l'at_ten_ _de_va!.... Già mi strug _
pay-ment. To-night's the night I've longed for: — Since — first — I —
ANDANTE APPASSIONATO MOLTO ♩= 69
p col canto
f
dim. molto
pp
rit.
lusingando
_gea l'a _ mor del _ la di _ va!... Ma po _
saw you, de - sire has con - sumed me, but to -
rit.

*poco affrett. a tempo*

SCAR.

_c'an _ zi ti mi _ ra _ _ i qual non ti vi _ di
night, _ though you hope to de - fy me, you can no more de -

*col canto. . . . . . a tempo*

(Rises in great emotion.)

SCAR.

ma _ _ i! Quel tuo pian _ to e _ ra
ny me. When you cried out de -

*p*

*cres.*

SCAR.

la _ _ va ai sen _ si mie _ i
spair - ing, pas - sion in - flamed me,

*f*

*dim.*

*lusingando* *a tempo*

SCAR.

e il tuo sguardo che o_dio in me dardeg - gia - - va, mie
and your glanc- es al- most drove be-yond bear - ing, the

*col canto* . . . . . . . . . . . . . . . . *a tempo*

SCAR.

bra _ me in _ fe _ ro _ ci _ _ va!
lust to which you've doomed me.

*affrett.*

*a tempo*

SCAR.

A _ gil qual le _ o _ par _ _ do t'av _ vinghia _ sti all' a _
How your hat - red en - hanc - es my re - solve to pos -

*a tempo*

poco allarg.
SOSTENUTO
SCAR.
-man - te
sess you.
Ah! In quel - l'i -
I may curse or
SOSTENUTO
poco allarg.
(Approaches Tosca, opening his arms. Tosca, who
SCAR.
stan - te t'ho giura - ta mia!
bless you, but you must be mine!
poco affrett.
TOSCA
Ah!
Ah!
has listened to Scarpia horrified and motionless, rises suddenly and takes refuge behind the sofa.)
SCAR.
Mia!
Mine!
Sì, t'avrò!
You are mine!
affrett. e cres.

Più SOSTENUTO
(Horrified, runs to the window.)
(Pointing to the window.)
T.
Ah!........................
Ah!
Ah!
Ah,
Piuttosto giù m'av-
I'd rath- er take my
SCAR.
Sì, t'avrò.......
You are mine!
48
Più SOSTENUTO
ff tutta forza
Mosso
-ven - - to!
life first.
Ah! mi - se -
How do you
In pegno il Ma-rio tuo mi re - sta!...
But how a- bout your dar- ling Ma- rio?
Mosso
ff

(She rushes to the door, intending to appeal to the Queen.)

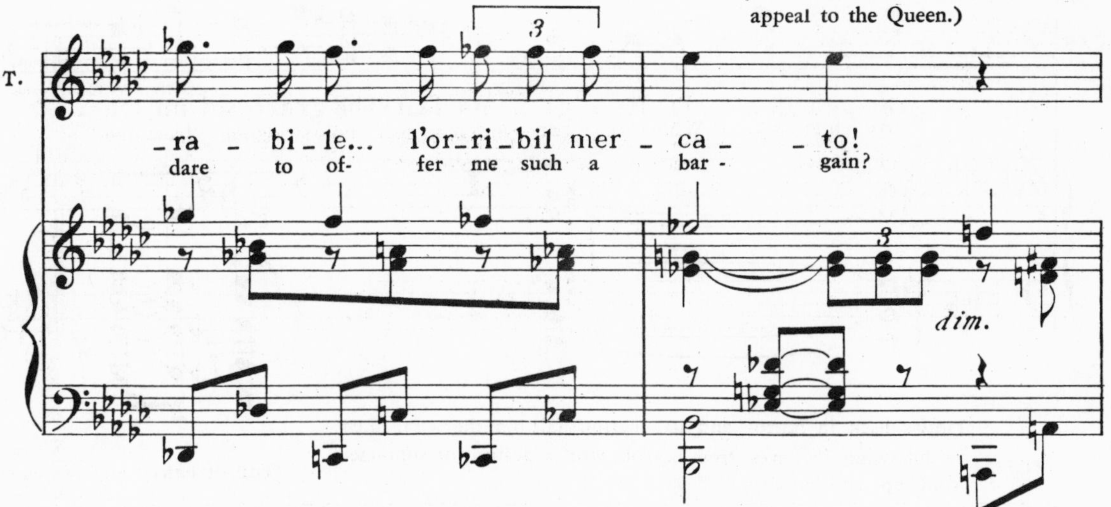

T.

3

_ra _ bi _ le... l'or_ri _ bil mer _ ca _ _ to!
dare to of- fer me such a bar - gain?

3

*dim.*

(Guessing her secret thought, he lets her pass.)

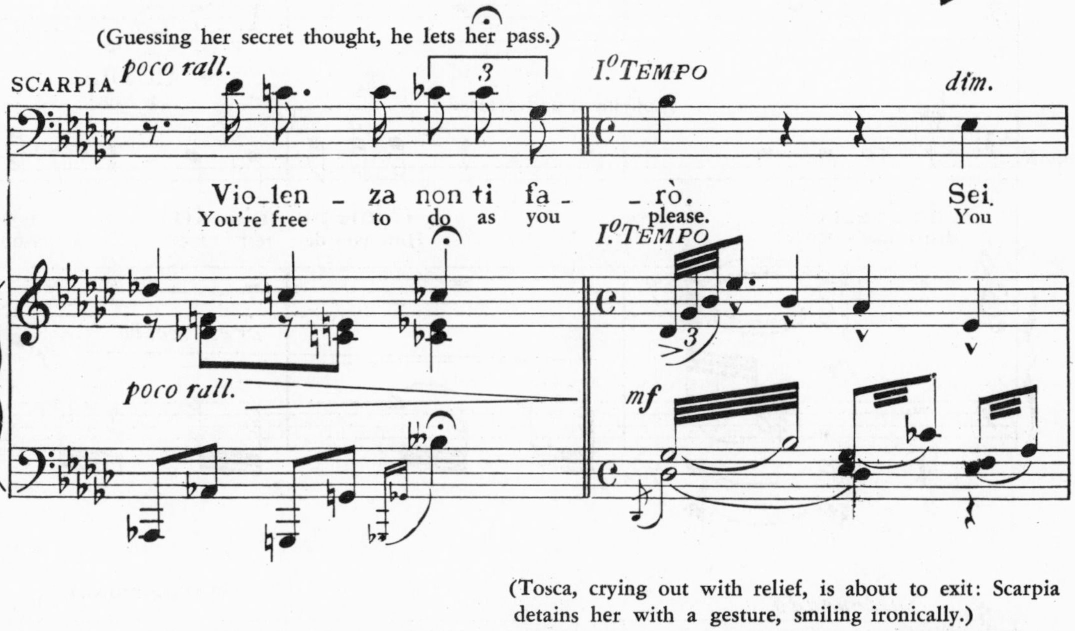

SCARPIA *poco rall.*

3

1°TEMPO *dim.*

Vio_len _ za non ti fa _ _ rò. Sei.
You're free to do as you please. You

1°TEMPO

3

*poco rall.*

*mf*

(Tosca, crying out with relief, is about to exit: Scarpia detains her with a gesture, smiling ironically.)

Meno
3
3
SCAR.
li _ be_ra. Va pu _ re. Ma è fal _ la _ ce spe _
want to leave? You're free to. But your queen can- not
Meno
3
*pp*

SCAR.
-ran-za:....... la Re-gi - na fa-rebbe grazia ad un ca -
save him. Who can par- don a man who's swing-ing from the
p
TOSCA
(Draws back in horror and lets herself fall on the sofa; then withdrawing her eyes from Scarpia with a gesture of supreme contempt and hatred.)
(Full of hatred and contempt.)
Ah! Dio!..
I do!
(Convinced and pleased.)
3
SCAR.
-da-ve-re!
hang-man's noose?
Come tu m'o-dii! Co
How you de- test me! And
pp
cres. molto
ff
Sostenendo
(In exasperation.)
T.
(Approaching her.)
Non toc-
Do not
SCAR.
49
-sì, co-sì ti vo-glio!
that's the way I want you!
Sostenendo
marcatissimo

Allegro
T.
_car_mi, demonio! T'o_dio, t'o_dio, t'o_dio, abbietto,
touch me, you mur-d'rer! How I hate you, hate you! You cow-ard,
Allegro
(Fleeing Scarpia in horror.)
vi - le!
mur - d'rer!
SCARPIA
Che impor_ta?!
De- test me!
ff
(Coming still closer.)
SCAR.
Spa_si_mi d'i_ra... spa_si_mi d'a_mo_re!
Passion-ate in hat-ing, pas-sion-ate in lov-ing.

(Behind the table.)
T.
Vi - le!
Mon - ster!
Vi - le!
Mur - d'rer.
(Trying to seize her.)
(Pursuing her.)
SCAR.
Mi - a!
To - sca!
Mi - a!
To - sca!
mf
cres. molto
LARGO
A - iu - to! A - iu - to! A -
I hate you! I hate you! I
50
(Shouting.)
(Yelling.)
Mi - a!
Tosca!
Mi - a!
Tosca!
LARGO
ff tutta forza
sostenendo
rit...
50

ALLEGRO ♩=132
(At the sound of the drums, both stand motionless.)
T.
-iu - to!
hate you!
(With emphasis.)
SCAR.
O - di? È il tam-bu - ro. S'av-
Lis - ten, hear the drum roll. You
(A drum roll is heard, slowly approaching.)
ALLEGRO ♩=132
p
SCAR.
-vi - a. Gui - da la scor - ta ul - ti-ma ai
hear it? This is the drum an - nounc - ing an
pp
p

(Tosca, having listened
SCAR.
con_dan_na_ti.
ex- e- cu- tion!
Il tem_po pas_sa!
There's not much time left.
mf
mf
with great anxiety, leaves the window and leans against the sofa, exhausted.)
SCAR.
Sai....... quale oscu_ra o_pra lag_giù si
Tell me: do you real- ly know what is go- ing
p come un lamento
SCAR.
com_pia?...
on there?
Là........
No?
si
They're
cres.
cres.

(Tosca makes a movement of frightened despair.)
SCAR.
driz_za un pa_ti_bo_lo.
hoist- ing the gal-lows there,
f
dim. e allontanandosi a poco a poco
f
dim.
mf come un lamento
(Approaching her.)
SCAR.
Al tuo
and your
sempre più dim.
f
mf come un lamento
SCAR.
Ma_ rio, per tuo vo_ler,...... non re_sta che u_
Ma- rio, whom you have doomed, will not see the
e sempre più allontanandosi
dim.
p
dim.

(Tosca, overcome with grief, falls back on the sofa.)

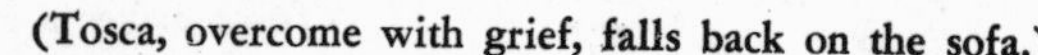

SCAR.
_n'o _ ra di vi _ ta.
sun of to- mor- row.
lontanissimi ..................
perdendosi ..................
p
rall.

(Scarpia, unimpressed, stands by the supper table, pours himself some coffee and drinks it, looking at Tosca all the while.)

e dim.
PPP più rall:... e morendo

AND.te LENTO APPASSIONATO ♩=40
TOSCA
dolcissimo con grande sentimento
p
51
Vis _ si d'ar _ te, vis _ si d'a _ mo _ re, non fe _ ci mai
Love for beau- ty, love and com- pas- sion, they gave to my
AND.te LENTO APPASSIONATO ♩=40
PP con molta dolcezza
PP

poco allarg.
con anima
T.
ma_le ad a_ni_ma vi_va!... Con man fur_ti_va quan_te mi
art its true in- spi- ra- tion. Sweet con- so- la- tion I brought to
ppp
f con anima
_se_rie co_nobbi, a_iu_ta_i...
those who are poor and un hap- py.
pp poco rall.
pp
52
con grande sentimento
p
Sem_pre........... con fè_ sin-
Al- ways with deep- e-
dolcissimo con grande sentimento
pp

T
_ce _ ra la mia pre _ ghie _ ra ai san_ti ta_ber
mo - tion, my true de - vo - tion I poured out to the
T
_ na_coli sa_lì. Sempre con fè...... since _ _ _ ra,
glo-ry of the Lord. I brought with deep_ de- vo - tion
pp
(Getting up.)
con anima
T
f
3p
die _ _ di fio _ ri a_gl'al _ tar,.......................... Nel_
flow - ers to a - dorn His house. De-
con anima
cres.
f

T.
l'o_ra del do_lo_re per_chè, perchè Si_gno_re, 'per
spair-ing of to-mor-row, my head is bowed in sor-row. Oh
pp
T.
_chè me ne ri_mu_ne_ri co_sì?
why, my Lord, with-draw Your Hand from me?
pp
T.
Die_di gio_iel_li del_la Ma_don_na al
My world-ly treas-ure I glad-ly laid on His
dolcissimo
ppp

T.
man - to, e die - di il can - to a gli astri, al ciel, che
al - tar; I'd nev - er fal - ter in sing - ing of His
T.
ne ridean più bel - li..........
Nel - l'o - ra del dolor per -
great-ness with-out meas-ure.
If love is doomed to die, Oh
cres. molto
T.
- chè, per - chè Si - gnor, ah,
Lord, my Lord, Tell me - why? Ah.
cres. molto
f molto allarg.

rall.
(Sobbing.)
sostenuto
T.
..............perchè me ne rimu - neri co - sì?
——Lord, why do You with-draw Your Hand from me?
SCARPIA
53
Ri-
Your
sostenuto
pp col canto
pp

(Kneeling before Scarpia.)
T.
Mi vuoi sup - plice ai tuoi pie_di?
On my knees I beg for mer- cy.
SCAR.
-solvi!
an - swer?

ALL.° AGITATO
(Sobbing.)
T
Ve - - di,.....
See me:
ALL.° AGITATO
pp
come un lamento
le man giun - te io stendo a te!.................
Like a beg- gar I lie be- fore you.
(Lifting her folded hands.)
Ec - co,......................
Hear me,
cres.
(In despair.)
Sostenuto
ve - di,......................
hear me.
e............ mer -
I'm de-
Sostenuto
f

(Humbly.)
rall.
T
cè......... d'un tuo det - to, vin - ta a-spet - to....
feat - ed, I im - plore you. Show me mer - cy.
p
dim.
rall:.......
SCARPIA
AND.te MOSSO ♩= 76
54
p Sei trop - po bel - la,
AND.te MOSSO You're much too love - ly,
pp
p
SCAR.
To - sca, e trop - po a -
To - sca. Such charm - ing
SCAR.
- man - te......................... Ce - do.
grac - es! Well then—

SCAR.

A mi - se - ro prez - zo
it seems I can't best you.

*f*

*appassionato*

SCAR.

tu, a me u - na vi - ta,
You win your Ma - rio;

*f*

(Getting up, showing her contempt.)

TOSCA

Va!
No,

*dolce*

SCAR.

*p*

io, a te chieggo un' i - stan - te!
I, a sin-gle night's em brac - es!

*p*

*p*

affrett.
T
va! Mi fai ri - brez - zo! Va! va!
no! How I de - test you. No, no!
f
f

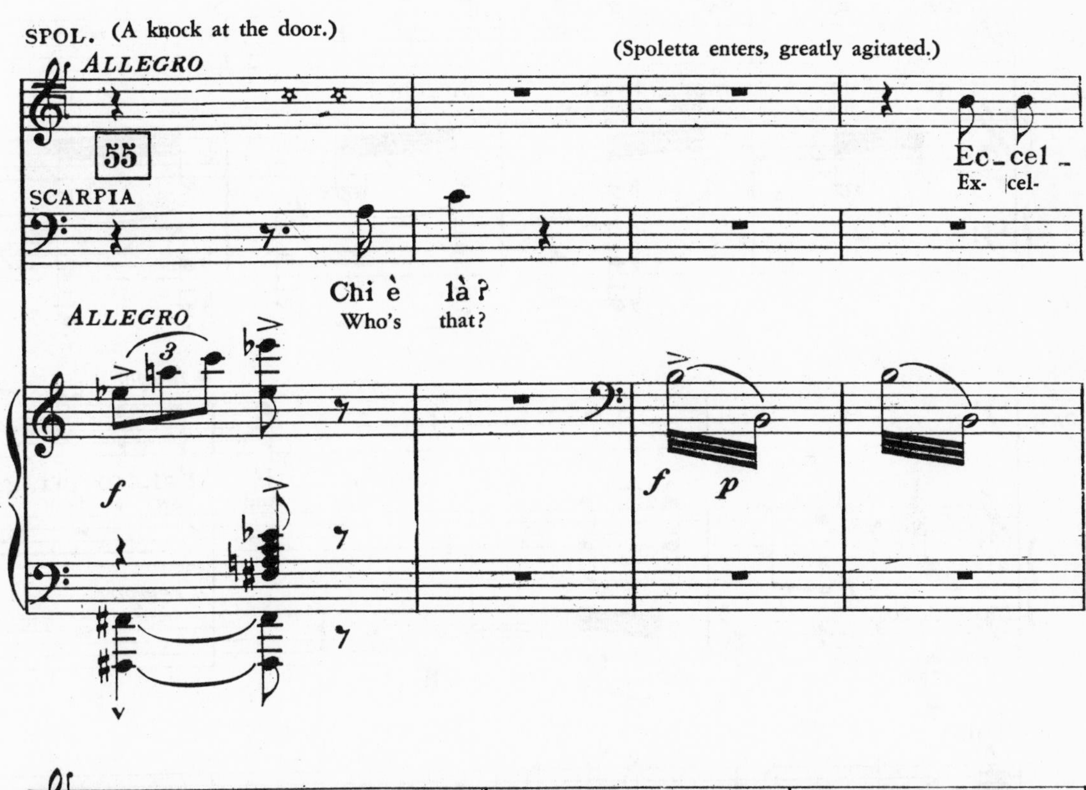
SPOL. (A knock at the door.)
(Spoletta enters, greatly agitated.)
ALLEGRO
55
Ec - cel -
Ex- cel-
SCARPIA
Chi è là?
Who's that?
ALLEGRO
f
f p

SPOL.
- len - za, l'An - ge - lot - ti al no - stro giun - ge - re s'uc -
len- cy, An- ge- lot- ti killed him- self be- fore we
p

SPOL.
_ci_se!
reached him.
SCAR.
Eb _ ben lo si ap-
All right. We will
ff deciso
SCAR.
_pen _ da mor _ to al_le for_che!
hang his corpse on the gal_lows.
f
p
SCAR.
a tempo
E l'al_tro pri_gio-
And how a- bout his
f
a tempo
SPOL.
Il ca_va_lier Ca_va_ra_dos_si?
You mean that man, Ca-va-ra-dos-si?
SCAR.
_nier?
friend?
f
3
f

TOSCA

(To herself.)

*a tempo*

(Dio! m'as - si - sti!)
God in Heav- en!

*a piacere*

SPOL.

È tut - to pronto, Eccel - len - za!
We shall pro- ceed as you or-dered.

*a tempo*

*col canto*

*mf* *p*

SCARPIA (To Spoletta.)

A - spet - ta.
One mo - ment.

*poco rall.*

(To Tosca, in a low voice.)

*pausa* *lento a piacere*

SCAR.

Eb - be - ne?
I'm wait - ing.

*pp*

(Nods "yes", then weeping for shame she buries her head in the cushions on the sofa.)
TOSCA
LENTO DOLOROSO
AND.te MOSSO
(Interrupting Scarpia.)
56
(To Spoletta.)
SCAR.
Ma
You
O - di...
Lis - ten.
LENTO DOLOROSO
espressivo
AND.te MOSSO
p
f
dim.
T
li - be-ro al-l'i - stan - te lo vo - glio!
prom- ise he'll be free be- fore morn - ing?
(To Tosca.)
quasi a piacere
Oc - cor - re si - mu -
That's more than I can
- lar. Non pos - so far gra - zia a - per - ta. Bi -
do. I've nev- er grant- ed a par-don! We

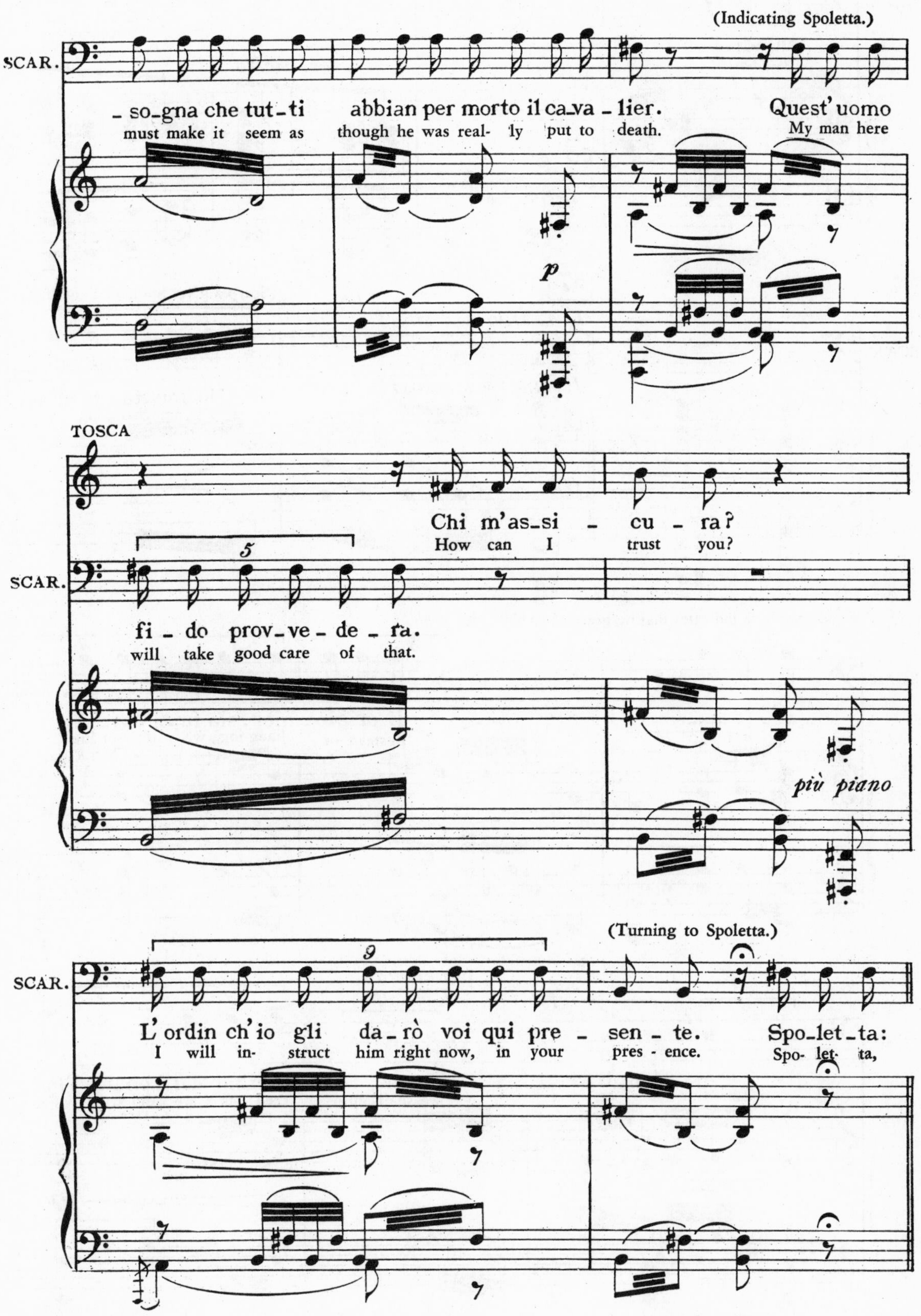
(Indicating Spoletta.)
SCAR.
-so-gna che tut-ti abbian per morto il ca-va-lier. Quest'uomo
must make it seem as though he was real-ly put to death. My man here
p
TOSCA
Chi m'as-si-cu-ra?
How can I trust you?
5
SCAR.
fi-do prov-ve-de-ra.
will take good care of that.
più piano
(Turning to Spoletta.)
9
SCAR.
L'ordin ch'io gli da-rò voi qui pre-sen-te. Spo-let-ta:
I will in-struct him right now, in your pres-ence. Spo-let-ta,

(Spoletta quickly closes the door and goes back to Scarpia.)

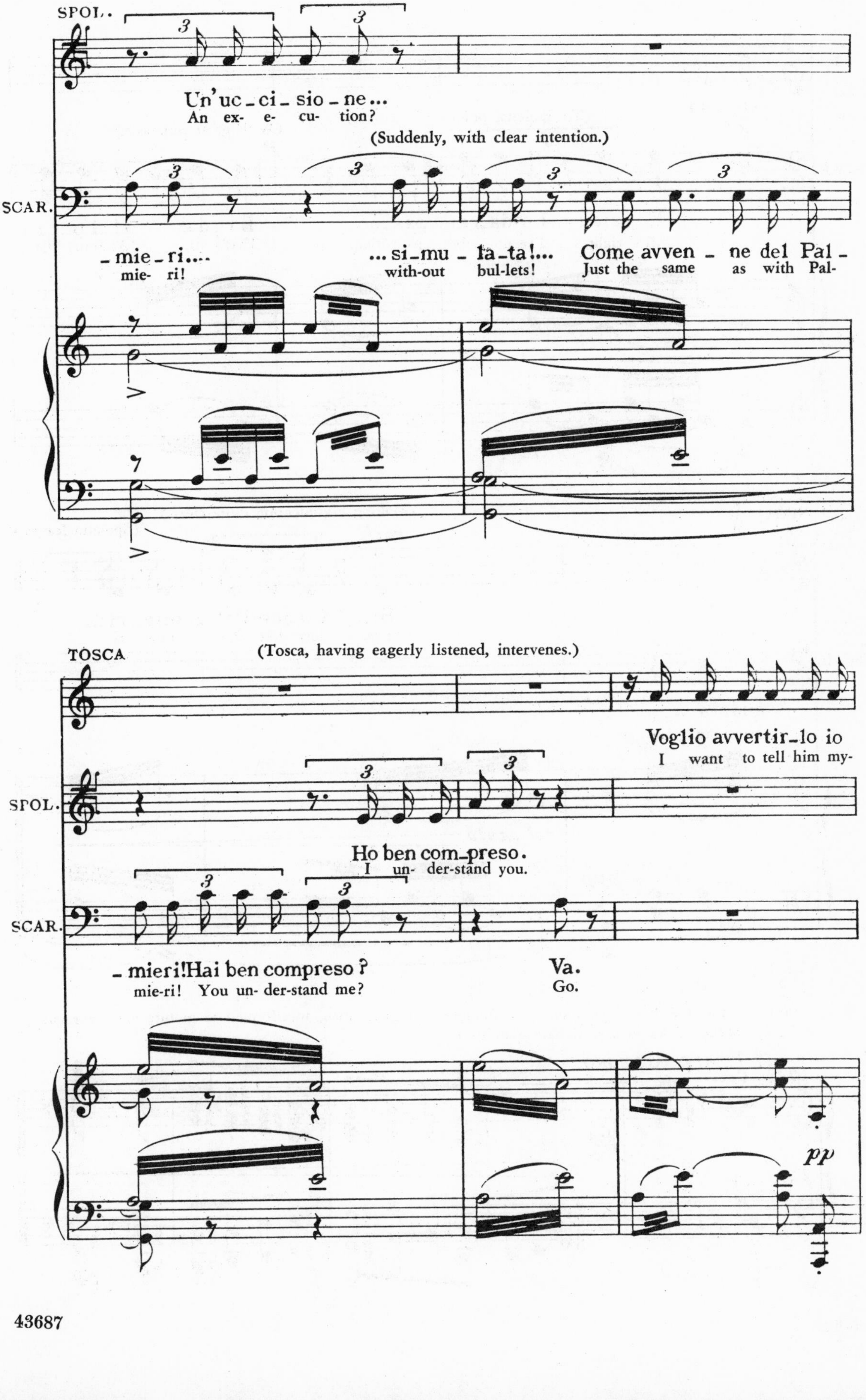

TOSCA (Tosca, having eagerly listened, intervenes.)

Voglio avvertir-lo io
I want to tell him my-

SPOL.

Ho ben com-preso.
I un-der-stand you.

SCAR.

-mieri! Hai ben compreso?
mie-ri! You un-der-stand me?

Va.
Go.

*pp*

T.

stes_sa.
self.

(To Spoletta, pointing at Tosca.)

(With great emphasis.)

SCAR.

*p*

3

E sia. Le da_rai pas_so. Ba_da: al_l'o_ra
All right, I've no ob- jec- tion. That's all. At four, this

SPOL.

(Making his intention quite clear.)

*rall.*

(Spoletta leaves.)

Sì. Co_me Pal _ mie_ri...
Yes, just like Pal mie- ri.

SCAR.

quarta...
morn-ing.

*col canto*

*ppp*

58

(Scarpia, near the door, makes sure that Spoletta has gone; then, transformed in gesture and expression, he approaches Tosca in a passionate outburst.)

TOSCA
*Andante*
(Stopping him.)
*quasi a piacere*
Non an-cora. Voglio un salvacon-
Not com-plete-ly. Give me some-thing in

SCARPIA
Io tenni la pro-messa...
You see, I've kept my prom-ise.

*Andante*
*ppp*
*col canto*

T.
-dotto on-de fuggir dallo Sta-to con lui.
writ-ing so that we can leave the coun-try at once.
*a tempo*

SCAR.
(Very courteously.)
*p* *dolce*
Par-tir dun-que vo-
You mean you want to

*a tempo*
*dolce*
*p*

T.
(With conviction.)
Si, per sem-pre!
Yes, for-ev-er!
*rall.*

SCAR.
-le-te?
leave us?
Si a-dem-pia il vo-ler
Your wish-es are my

*espressivo*
*col canto*
*pp*
*pp*

(Goes to his desk and writes.)
SCAR.
vo _ stro.
or - ders.
AND.te SOSTENUTO ♩=52
59
AND.te SOSTENUTO ♩=52
tratt:
ppp
TOSCA
p
La più breve!
By the short-est.
SCARPIA
(Looking up from his writing, he asks Tosca:)
p
E qual via sce_gliete?
Which way will you trav-el?
Civita_
You mean by
ppp

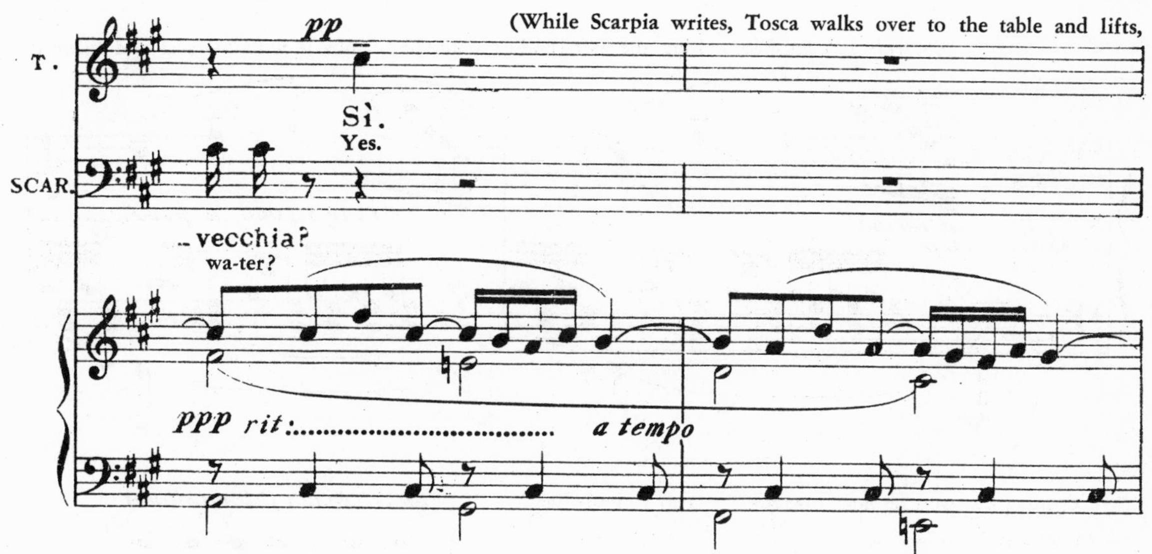
(While Scarpia writes, Tosca walks over to the table and lifts,
pp
T.
Sì.
Yes.
SCAR.
..vecchia?
wa-ter?
ppp rit:
a tempo

with a trembling hand, the glass that Scarpia had filled; while doing so, she sees the knife on the table;

ten.
animando
stent:
p
rall:

after a furtive glance at Scarpia, who is still writing, she grasps the knife and very cautiously hides it behind

sostenendo
f
rit.

her back, leaning against the table and still glancing at Scarpia.)

sempre sostenuto e rall. molto
espressivo
pp rit.

(Scarpia has finished writing the safe-conduct note; he stamps it with his seal and folds it;

60
a tempo
pp
string: poco a poco


opening his arms he goes towards Tosca to embrace her.)

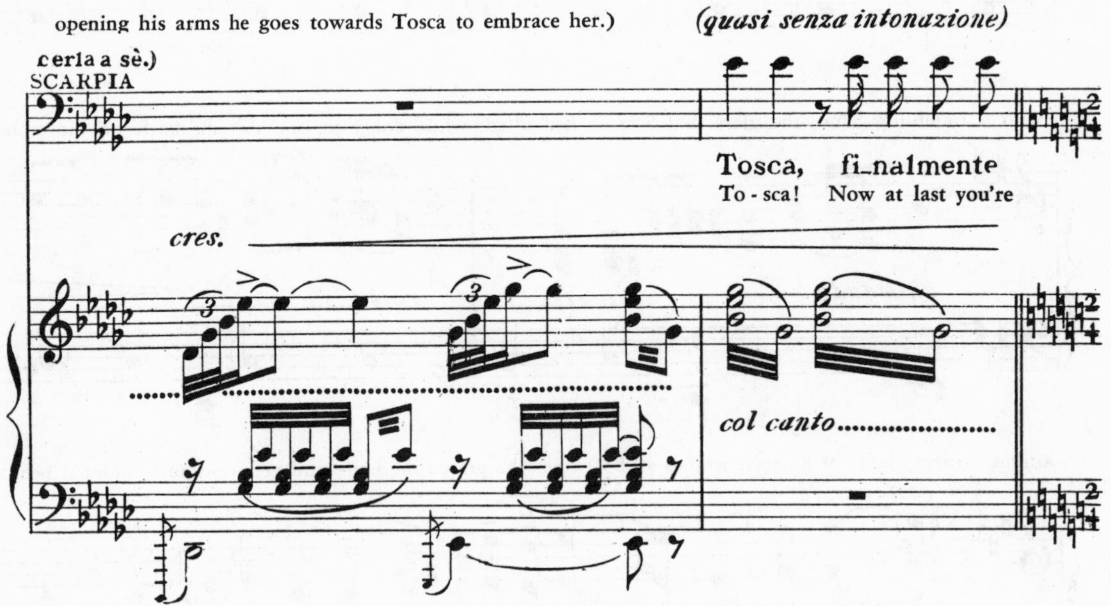
(quasi senza intonazione)
cerla a sè.)
SCARPIA
Tosca, fi_nalmente
To-sca! Now at last you're
cres.
col canto

ALL° NON TROPPO, ma con violenza. ♩= 160
(Tosca stabs him.)
SCAR.
mia!
mine!
ALL° NON TROPPO, ma con violenza. ♩= 160
ff

TOSCA

(Shouting.)

Questo è il
That's the

SCAR.

(Shouting.)

Ma - le - det - ta!!
*ruvido* You as- sas- sin!

*ff*

*ff*

T.

ba - cio di To - sca!
way To - sca kiss - es!

(With a breaking voice.)

(Staggering, he tries

SCAR.

*f*

A - iu - to! Muoio!
I'm dy - ing, help me!

*sempre ff*

3

3

to get hold of Tosca, who withdraws in horror.)

*più forte*

SCAR.

*f*

Soc - cor - so! Muo - io!
I'm dy - ing, help me!

3

3

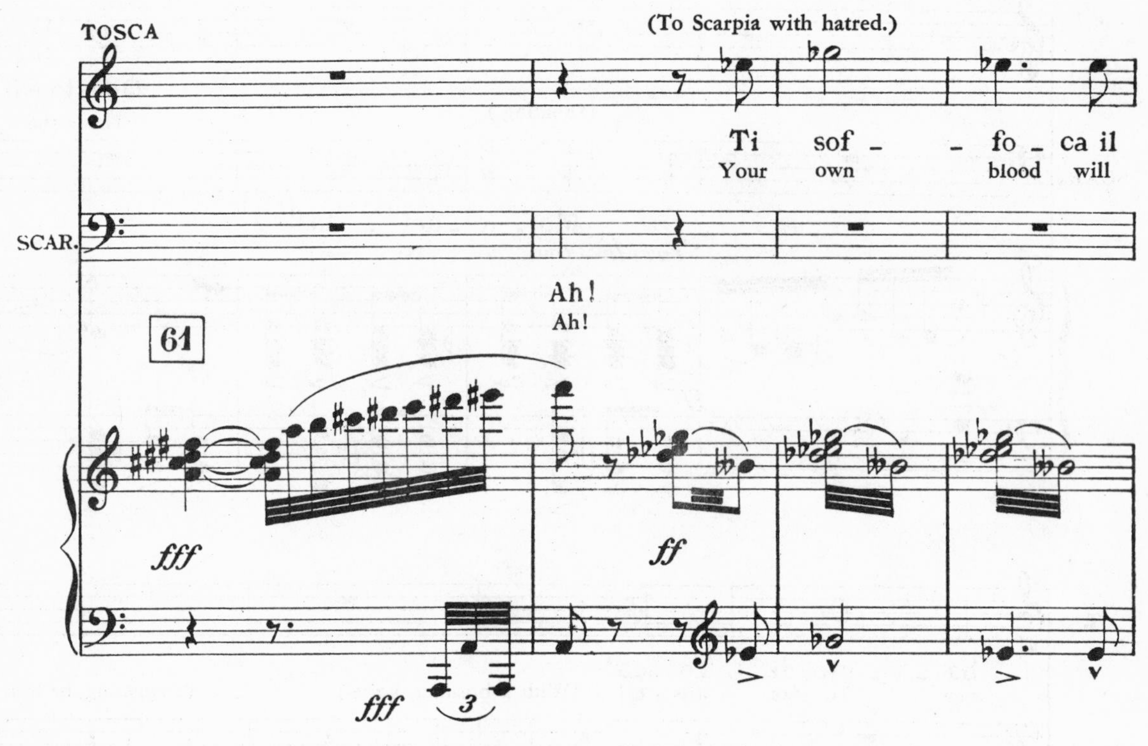
TOSCA
(To Scarpia with hatred.)
Ti sof - - fo - ca il
Your own blood will
SCAR.
Ah!
Ah!
61
fff
ff
fff
3

T.
sangue?
choke you.
Ti sof - fo - ca il sangue?
Your own blood will choke you.
(Choking.)
(Tries in vain to rise, clutching the sofa.)
SCAR.
Soc - corso!
I'm dy - ing.
A -
I'm
3

T.
Ah!......
Ah. —
E uc - ci - so da una
It's To - sca who has
SCAR.
- iu - to!...
dy - ing.
Muoio,
Help me!
muoio!
Help me!
dim.

T.
don - na!
killed you.
M'hai as - sai tor - tu - ra - ta!...
Now you pay for my torture!
SCAR.
A - iu - to!
I'm dy - ing.
Soc - cor - so!
I'm dy - ing!
dim. sempre

poco rall:
T.
Odi tu an_cora? Parla!.. Guardami!..Son Tosca!.. o
Can you still hear me? An-swer! Look at me! Look Scar-pia, it's
(Scarpia makes one last effort, then falls on his back.)
SCAR.
muoio!
Help me!
dim. sempre più
poco rall:
AND.te TETRO (lo stesso movimento)
T.
Scarpia!!
To - sca!
Ti soffoca il sangue?
Your own blood will choke you.
SCAR.
62
Soccorso, a _ iu_to!
I'm dy - ing, I'm dy - ing,
Muoio!
dy- ing—
AND.te TETRO (lo stesso movimento)
pp
pp
(Bending over Scarpia.)
con ferocia
con forza crescente
T.
Muori dan _ nato! Muori, muori, muori!
Die in dam- na-tion! Scar-pia! Scar-pia! Die now!
pp
ppp

T.

È mor_to!
He's dead.

(Remains motionless.)

SCAR.

Ah!.....
Ah!

*And.te* ♩ = 52

(Without taking her

T.

Or gli per – – do – no!
Now I for- – – give him.

*And.te* ♩ = 52

63 *ff*

eyes off Scarpia, Tosca takes the water pitcher, pours out some water, and cleans her fingers with a napkin; then she arranges her hair before the mirror.)

(Remembering the safe-conduct note, she searches the desk for it but does not find it;

finally she sees it in the hand of Scarpia.)

(She lifts Scarpia's arm which she lets fall again after having taken the safe-conduct note out of his hand; she hides the document in her bodice.)

(About to leave, she changes her mind:
T.
E avanti a lui tremava tutta Ro_ma!
This is the man be-fore whom all Rome trem-bled.
64
sostenuto
she takes the two candlesticks, lights them with the candelabra on the table and then extinguishes
T.
3
m.d.
3
the latter.)
T.
trattenuto
3
3
rall:
rit:
pp

(She places the two candles on either side of Scarpia's head.)

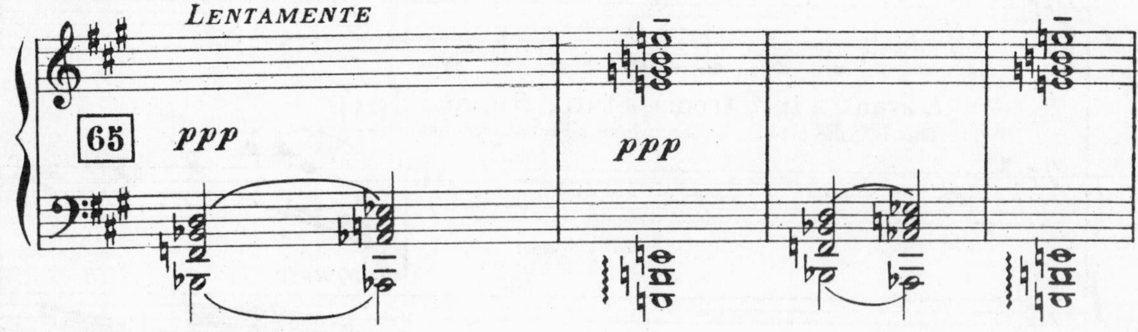


(Looking around she sees a crucifix: she lifts it from the wall and, carrying it, she kneels religiously and puts the crucifix on Scarpia's chest.)

(Drums are heard in the distance.)

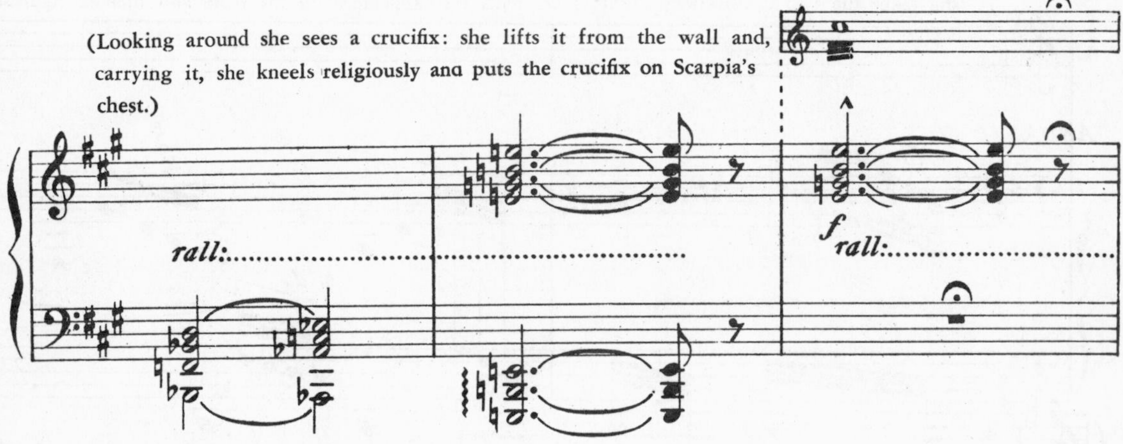


(She rises and leaves the room very cautiously, closing the door behind her.)

*Fine dell'Atto II°*

# ACT III

## CASTEL SANT'ANGELO

(To the left a prison cell, a bench, a chair, a table, on it a lamp, the prison register, and writing utensils. On the wall a crucifix, with a light in front of it. On the right, the opening of a stairwell which gives access to the platform. In the distance, the Vatican and St. Peter's Basilica.)

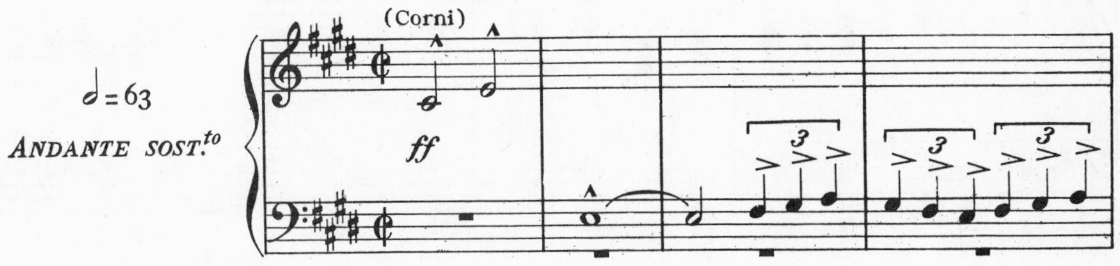

(Night. A clear sky, sparkling with stars.)
(The curtain rises.)
1
pp
pp
Sostenendo
p
pp
p poco rall:...
a tempo
m.s.

2
ff
p
tr
f
mf
accelerando
accelerando

(In the distance sheepbells are heard, gradually fading away.)

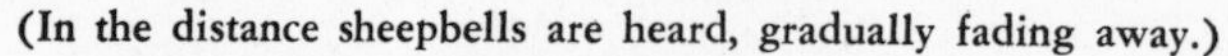

UN PASTORE [A YOUNG SHEPHERD]
a voce spiegata, ma molto lontano
UN POCO MENO
3
UN POCO MENO
ppp
Io de' so - spi - ri,
Wind, hear my sor-row,
ppp

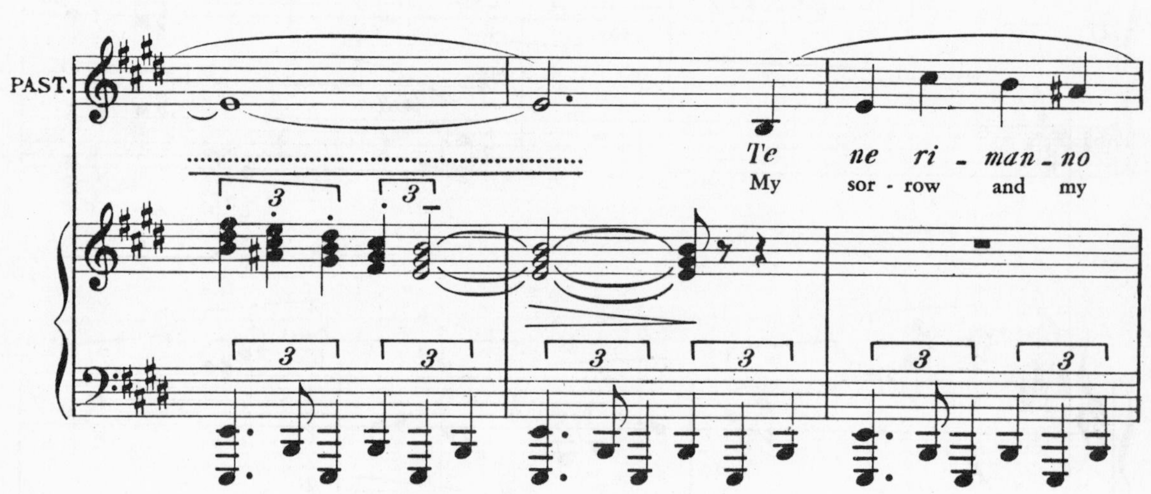
PAST.
Te ne ri - man - no
My sor - row and my

(The bells, still farther away, are heard at irregular intervals.)
PAST.
tan - ti
sigh - ing

PAST.
Pe' quan - te fo - je
like leaves in autumn
Come prima 𝅗𝅥 = 63
PAST.
Ne smo - ve - no li ven - ti.
that fade and fall in dy - ing.
𝅗𝅥 = 63
Come prima
pp
PAST.

(The bells are dying away in the distance.)
Sostenendo
PAST.
Tu mme di - sprez - zi Io me ciac - co - ro,
Say that our vows have not been bro - ken.
Sostenendo
PAST.
perdendosi
(The light is
Lam - pena d'o - ro Me fai mo - rir!
Send me a to- ken, else I must die.
pp
p sostenen.
uncertain and grey; it is just before dawn.)
pp rall:

4
Lento 𝅗𝅥 = 40
(The matin bells.)
(Very far away.)
(Closer.)
(Church bells
at various distances.)
Lento 𝅗𝅥 = 40
pppp
(Nearby.)
(Farther away.)
(Far away.)

(A jailer, with a lantern, climbs up the stairs; enters the prison cell and lights the lamp before the

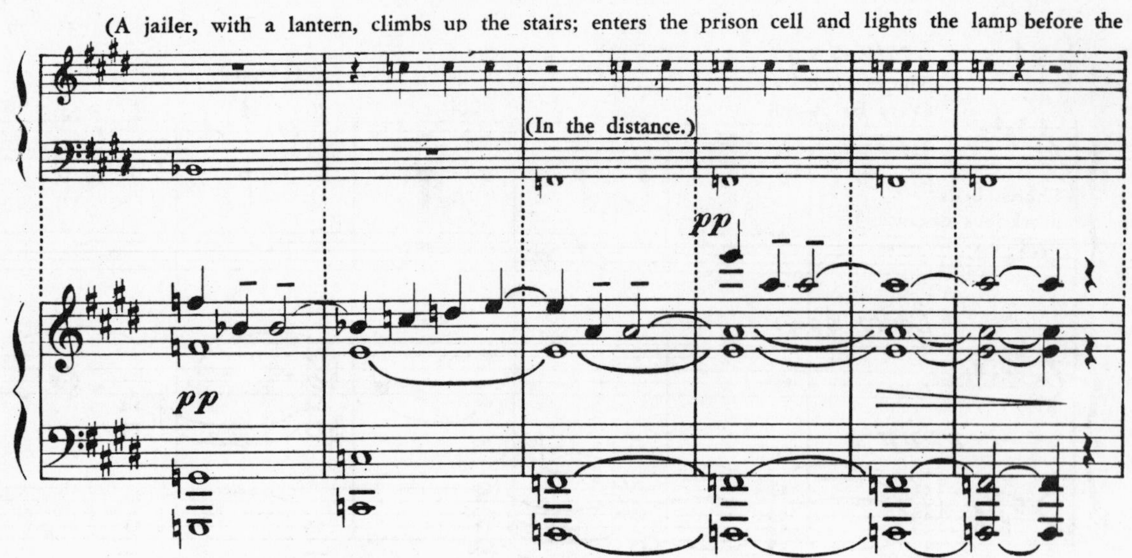


crucifix, then the one on the table. He walks to the railing and looks down into the courtyard to see

whether the firing squad and the condemned man are arriving. He meets a sentry who is crossing the

platform; after having exchanged some words with him, he returns to the cell; sits down, waiting, half-asleep.)

(Very far away.)

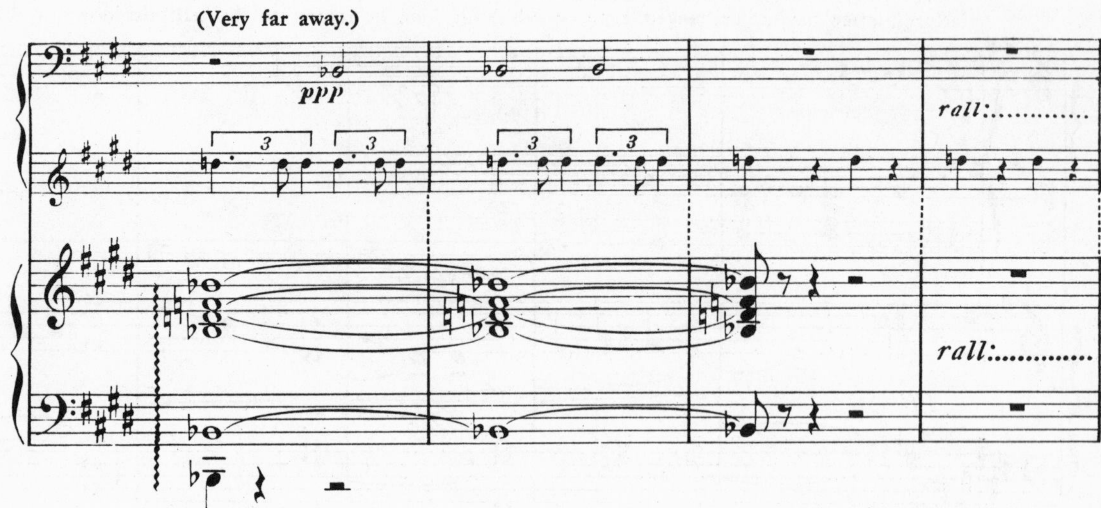


(A group of soldiers, led by a sergeant, arrives on the platform, escorting Cavaradossi.

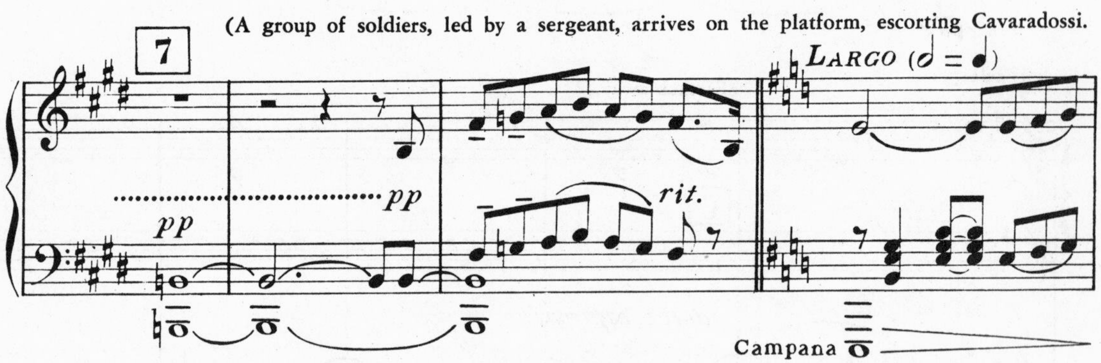


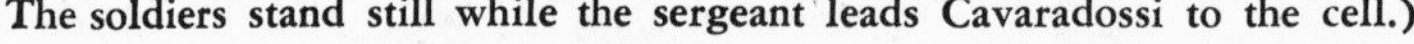

The soldiers stand still while the sergeant leads Cavaradossi to the cell.)

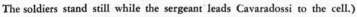

(Seeing the sergeant, the jailer gets up and salutes; the sergeant hands him a sheet of paper which

f con molta anima
p

he examines. He sits down at the table, opens the register and writes while speaking to Cavaradossi.)

8
f
ten.
rall. molto
ten.

(Cavaradossi nods in affirmation.)

(He hands a pen to the sergeant, who signs the register and leaves, followed by his soldiers.)

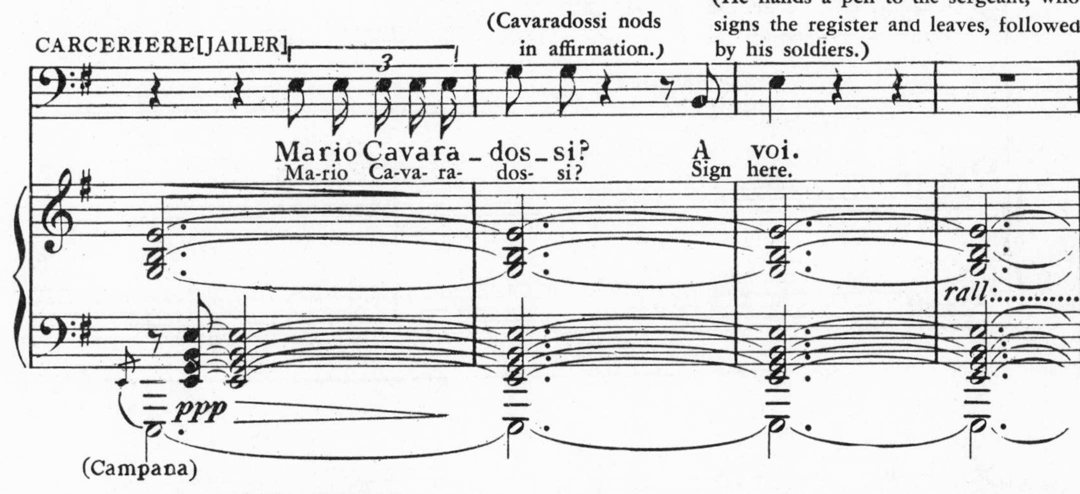
CARCERIERE [JAILER]
Mario Cavara_dos_si? A voi.
Ma-rio Ca-va-ra- dos- si? Sign here.
rall:
ppp
(Campana)

(To Cavaradossi.)

p lentamente
CARC.
Vi resta u_n'ora... Un sacer_do_te i vostri cenni at_tende.
You have an hour. A priest is wait-ing if you should like to see one.
col canto

ANDANTE LENTO
CAVARADOSSI
No.
Ma u_n'ul_ti_ma gra_zia io vi ri_
No.
But I'd like to ask you for one last
9
ANDANTE LENTO
con sentimento
rall.
CAV.
_chiedo...
fa- vor.
Io lascio al mon_do u_na per_so_na
I leave be- hind me some-one I love and
CARC.
Se posso...
What is it?
rall:
CAV.
ca_ra.
cher- ish.
dolce, sostenuto e legato
(Violoncelli)
pp

CAV.
Consen-ti-te ch'io le scriva un sol motto.
I would like to say fare-well in a let-ter.
ppp
p
(Taking a ring off his finger.)
tristamente
CAV.
U-ni-co re-sto di mia ric-chez-za è questo a-
All I have left of my earth-ly wealth is this lit-tle
CAV.
-nel...
ring
Se pro-met-te-te di con-se-
If you will prom-ise me to make
rit.

CAV.
-gnar-le il mio ul-ti-mo ad-di-o, es-so e
cer- tain that my note is de- liv- ered, you may
p
CAV.
vo - stro...
keep it.
CARC. (After a slight hesitation, he accepts and motions to Cavaradossi to sit down.)
10
Scri-
All
f
(Sitting on the bench.)
MENO
CARC.
-ve-te.
right, then.
MENO
dolcissimo espressivo
p (Violoncelli)

(Cavaradossi is deep in thought; then begins to write.)

cres.
allarg.
cres. ed allarg.
f
(He writes a few lines but, overcome by his memories, he interrupts
p
rit.
f
accel.
rall. e dim.
his writing.)
11
dolcissimo, vagamente
rubando
p rall.
p
rit.

ANDte LENTO APPASSIONATO MOLTO

CAVAR.
(Remembering.)
E lu_ce_van le stel_le...
I re-mem- ber the star- light
rit:....... rubando rit:........

CAV.
e olezza_va la terra, stridea l'uscio del _ l'orto...
and the per-fume of ros- es, a gar-den gate that o-pened,
stent.
a tempo
mf

CAV.
e un pas_so sfio_ra_va la re_na...
a foot- step as soft as an an- gel's,
p
CAV.
En_trava ella, fragrante,
I felt her fra-grant pres-ence...
sostenendo vagamente
mf
m.s.
m.d.
CAV.
affrett.
rit. ed appassionato
mi ca_dea fra le brac_cia...
we were lost in each oth- er.
12
rit.
m.d.
affrett.
f

con grande sentimento
(vagamente)
CAV.
Oh! dol_ci ba_ci, o languide ca _ rez_ze, mentr'io fre_
A night of kiss- es, pas-sion- ate ca- ress- es, my hands were
con grande sentimento
pp
_men _ te le bel_le for _ me discio_gliea dai ve _ li!
trem- bling to hold your love- li- ness in sweet sur- ren- der.
rit.
Svanì per sempre il sogno mio d'a_mo_re... l'ora è fug_ gi _ ta..............
For-ev- er now my dream of love is end-ed, and when the day breaks

stentato un poco
con anima
CAV.
..... e muoio di - spe - ra - to!...
I die in des - per - a - tion,
e muoio di - spe -
I die in des - per -
f con anima
stentato un poco
Sostenuto e cres. con slancio
rit.
- ra - to!
a tion;
E non ho amato mai tanto la vita, tanto la
and nev - er was so much in love with liv-ing, in love with
Sostenuto e cres. con slancio
13
rit. col canto
affrett.
m.s.
m.d.
Lento (He bursts into tears, burying his face in his hands.)
vita!.....
liv-ing!
Lento
pp
rall.

(Spoletta comes up the stairs with the sergeant, followed by Tosca: the sergeant carries a lantern.

Spoletta shows Tosca where she can find Cavaradossi, then calls the jailer; with him and the sergeant

he walks down the stairs again, after having beckoned to the sentry to keep an eye on the prisoner.)

(Tosca, who has been in a state of great excitement, sees Cavaradossi crying. She rushes up to him, but unable to speak for emotion, she raises his head with her hands and shows him the safe-conduct note. Cavaradossi, seeing Tosca, gets up in great surprise; then reads the document.)

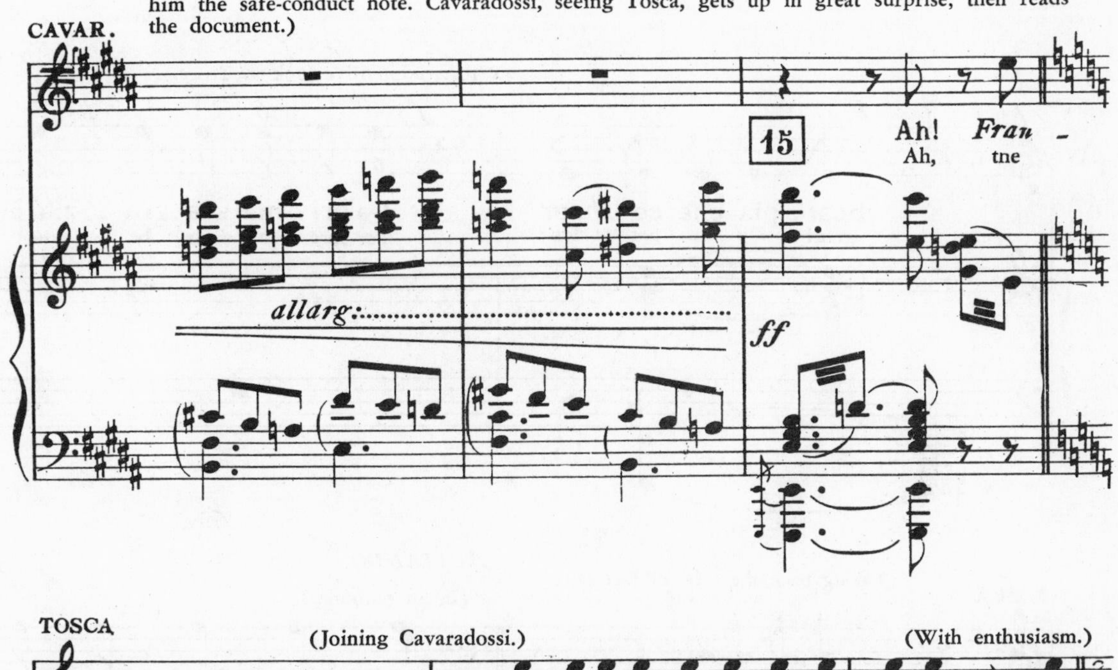

T.
li - - - be - ro!
safe at last!
(Looks and reads the signature.)
CAV.
Scar_pia!...
Scar - pia,
(With an intensive look at Tosca.)
CAV.
Scar_pia che ce_de?
grant- ing a par- don?
La pri_ma sua gra_zia è
I'm sure that must be the
(Taking back the safe-conduct note.)
TOSCA
E l'ul_ti_ma.
Al-so the last!
AGITANDO
(In an outburst.)
Il tuo san_gue o il mio a_
"Love me, To- - sca or
CAV.
questa....
first time!
Che di_ci?...
What hap-pened?
16
AGITANDO

T.
mo - re volea...
Fur va - - -
Ma - rio must die."
In vain

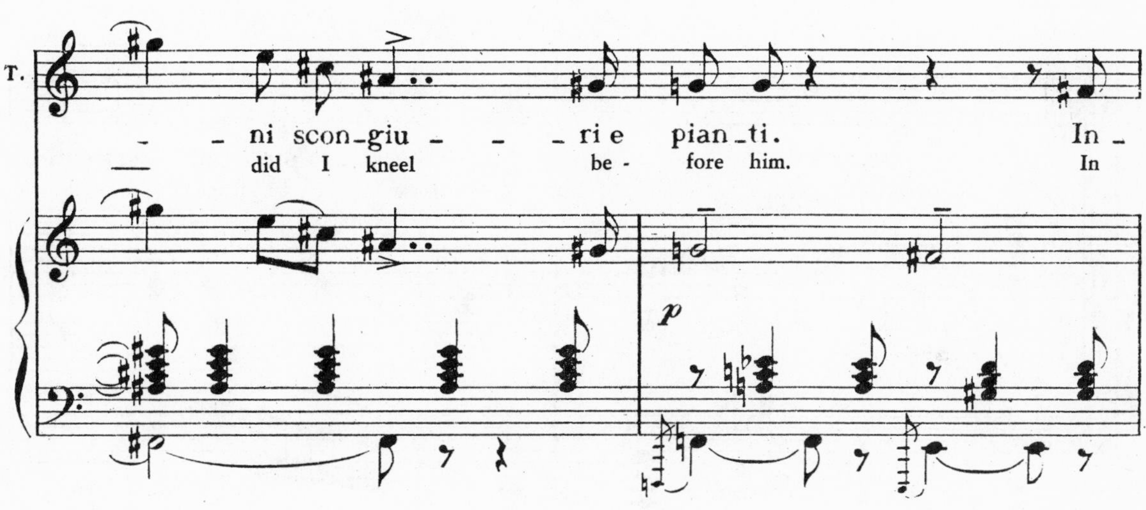
T.
- - ni scon-giu - - - ri e pian-ti.
In -
did I kneel be- fore him.
In
p

T.
3
van, paz - za d'or - ror, ............ al - la Ma -
vain, mad- dened with fear, I of- ferèd

T.
don - na mi vol - si e ai San - ti....
prayers up to God to im - plore Him.
p
T.
L'em - pio mo - stro di -
How he laughed when he
f
p
T.
ce - a: Già nei cie - li il pa - ti - bol le brac - cia
told me: "When the day breaks, they'll pre - pare him to mount the
pp
cres.

T.
le - va!
gal - lows."
Rul - la - va - no i tam -
I heard a muf - fled
17
f
p

T.
- bu - ri....
drum roll
Ri - - de - va, l'em - pio mo - stro.... ri -
and, laugh - ing, how the mon - ster was
p

T.
- de - va.... già la sua pre da pron - to a gher -
laugh - ing, wait - ing to lay his hands on his

T.
_mir!.......
prey!
«Sei
"You're
string.
f
T.
mi_
mine
_a?»
now!"
sempre string. e cres.
T.
-Si.-
Yes.
Alla sua bra_ma mi pro_mi_ _si
I let him think that I was yield - ing.
ff

T.
18
Lì pres_so luc_ci_
And then I saw a
a tempo
ff
_ca _ va u _ na la _ ma..........................
knife ___ on the ta - ble. ___
Ei scrisse il
He signed the
p
fo _ glio li _ be _ ra _ tor,..............
pa - per that set us free. ___

T.
ven _ ne all' or _ ren_do am_
As he ap-proached to
string.
T.
_ples_ _ _so......
kiss me,
e cres.
T.
rall.
Io quel _ la la_ _ _ma gli pian_tai nel
I plunged the knife into his e - vil
f
col canto.

MOLTO MENO
T.
cor.
heart.
CAVAR.
rall.
Tu?.... di tua man l'ucci - de_sti!-, tu pia tu be_ni_gna e per
You? It was you who de-stroyed him? My dar- ling, so gen- tle and so
19
rall.
rall. . . .
T.
N'eb_bi le man tut_te lor_de di sangue!...
Yes, I have killed him. My hands both are blood- stained.
(Taking Tosca's hands in his own.)
teneramente
CAV.
me!
kind?
O dolci
Your hands, so
p rall. . . . .
AND.no SOST.to
CAV.
ma - ni mansu - e_te e pu - re, o ma_ni e_
love - ly, love- li- er than flow- ers, were made for
pp

dolcissimo
poco rit.

CAV.

_let _ te a bell' o_pre e pie _ to _ se, a ca_rez_
la - bors of de-vout de- di- ca- tion; to soothe a

m.d. 3 m.s. m.d. col canto

allarg. . . .

a tempo

CAV.

_zar fan_ciul_li, a...... coglier ro _ se, a pre_gar,
cry- ing child and bring it con- so- la - tion; to pray for

espressivo

m.s.

a tempo allarg. . . .

**20**

ten. ten. a tempo
p

CAV.

giun _ _ te per le sven _ tu _ re, dun_que in
sun- shine through wind and show - ers. In these

ten.

P a tempo

col canto

CAV.
voi, fatte dall'a_mor se_cu_re, giu_sti_zia le sue
hands, steadied by a lov- er's pow- ers, the Lord has laid the
sa_cre ar_mi de_po_se?
weap-on of li- be- ra- tion!
ritenuto
dolciss.
Voi deste mor_te, o man vit_torïo_se, o dol_ci
You took his life — with a holy ex- ul- ta-tion, Your hands so
21
col canto...

Iº TEMPO
molto rall:.....
CAV.
ma - ni man-su-e-te e pu - re!...
love - ly, love- li- er than flow - ers.
Iº TEMPO
p
molto rall:.....
AND.no MODERATAMENTE MOSSO.
TOSCA
(Withdrawing her hands.)
(Pointing to her bag.)
a piacere
p
Senti... l' ora è vi - ci - na; io già rac - col - si o - ro e gio-
Lis-ten, there's not much time left. I brought some mon - ey, al- so my
22
AND.no MODERATAMENTE MOSSO.
col canto...........
p
T
-iel - li... u - na vet - tu - ra è pron - ta............ Ma
jew - els. A car- riage will be wait - ing. But

T
pri_ma... ri_di a_mor....... pri_ma sarai fu_ci_
first — I know you will laugh! — first they will shoot you for
T
_la_to.............. per fin_ta.............. ad ar_mi
trea- son! For Scar-pia must keep up ap-
T
sca_ri_che... Si_mu_la_to sup_pli_zio.
pear- anc-es. Yes, a mock ex- e- cu- tion!
p

UN POCO MENO.
allarg.
T
Al colpo... cadi. I sol_da_ti sen van_no... e noi siam
They'll fire — fall down. They will leave soon there- af- ter. We'll be u-
UN POCO MENO.
col canto...........
p
rall:...... quasi a piacere
sal - - vi, e noi siam sal - - vi! Poscia a Ci_vita_
nit - ed and_ free for- e - ver. Once we have crossed the
f
p rall: col canto....................
_vec_chia... u_na tar - ta_na... e via pel
bor- der we'll find a sail- boat and off to
mf

ANDANTINO SOSTENUTO.
T
mar!..
sea!
Li_beri!
Lib- er-ty!
CAVAR.
Liberi!
Lib-er-ty!
Via pel mar!
You and I.
23
ANDANTINO SOSTENUTO.
3
PP ondeggiando
T
Chi si duo_le inter_ra più?.......
All this hor- ror left be- hind.
P dolce
Sostenendo
a tempo
T
Sen _ ti efflu_vi di ro _ se?...
Gone the sor-row that bound us.
Non ti
Don't you
Sostenendo.........................
a tempo
pp

rall. e dim:.....
T
par che le co_se aspet_tan tut_te in_na_mo_
feel how all a - round us dreams of beau - ty, trem-bling be-
col canto rall. e dim.
molto rall.
ANDANTE AMOROSO ♩=56
T
_ra _ te il so _ le?..........................
CAVAR.
fore the sun- rise?
(With tenderest emotion.)
dolciss.
A_ma_ro sol per
The thought of dy- ing
24
ANDANTE AMOROSO ♩=56
molto rall:...
pp
CAV.
te m'e_ra il mori _ re, Da te la vi _ ta prende ogni splen-
tore my heart a - sun - der, to part from you, who gives my life its

cres.
CAV.
_do_re, all'es_ser mio la gioia ed il de _ si _ re........
splen- dor. It's you that fills my life with joy and won - der.
cres.
CAV.
na_scon di te, co_me di fiamma ar_ do _ re.
Love is the light that makes the dark sur - ren - der.
pp
CAV.
Io fol_go_ra_re i cie_li e sco_lo_ri _ re ve_
Like glitt' - ring stars when win - ter's night is fal - ling, your

CAV.
_drò nell'oc_chio tuo ri_ve_la _ to _ re, e la bel_
ra- diant eyes are full of re- ve- la- tion. All things that
p
Sostenendo
ten.
CAV.
_tà del_le co_se più mi_re a_vrà...... sol...... da
beau- ty has ren-dered en- thrall- ing, in your eyes they
Sostenendo
ten.
allarg. e cres.
con anima
TOSCA
A _ mor.......... che sep_pe a
My love, that saved your
rit.
CAV.
te............. vo _ ce e co _ lo _ re.
find their con - se - cra - tion.
25
rit. con anima f

T
te vi_ta ser_ba_re ci sa_rà gui_da in ter_ra,
life with its de- vo- tion, will be a shin- ing light wher-
pp
T
e in mar nocchier...... e va_go fa_
ev- er we go. Love will make us
pp
T
_rà il mon_do riguar_da_re.................................
see the world with a new e- mo- tion.
mf
p

SOSTENENDO
T.
Finchè congiunti al_le ce_le_sti sfe_re di_legue-
Till to the sink- ing sun we'll be as- cend- ing; freed from all
26
SOSTENUTO
p
rall:............................ a tempo
(As though in a vision.)
p
_rem, siccome al_te sul ma_re........................ a sol ca_dente,
bonds, like clouds that float a-bove the o- cean. There will be on- ly
a tempo
rall:............................
PP dolcissimo
più piano
PP morendo
nu_vole legge_re, nu_vole legge_re, nu_vole legge_re!...
hap-pi-ness un- end- ing, hap-pi-ness un- end- ing, hap-pi-ness un- end- ing.
dim. e morendo sempre

(Brought back to reality, Tosca looks around nervously.)
(They remain in silence, moved.)
ANDno MOSSO
T.
27
E non
They're not
ANDno MOSSO
ppp
(To Cavaradossi, with great tenderness.)
giungono....
coming yet
Ba_da!...
Mario,
al col_po e_gli è me-
re mem ber you must pre-
pp
_stie_re che tu su_bito
ca_da..........
CAVAR. tend they are shoot-ing you in
ear- nest.
(Sadly.)
Non te_me_re
I'll re- mem- ber.

CAV.
che ca_drò sul mo _ men _ to.... e al na_tu _
I will fall when they fire, just as you
TOSCA
(Urgently.)
Ma stammi at _ ten _ to di non far_ti
But please be care - ful, don't get hurt in
CAV.
_ ra _ le.
told me.
p
T.
rall.
ma _ le! Con sceni_ca scïen _ za io sa_prei la mo_
fall - ing! All ac- tors can do it. If I on- ly could
p rall:
e dim:
pp

MOLTO MENO
T.
_ven _ za...
show you.
(Interrupts her, drawing her towards him.)
CAV.
p dolce
Parlami an - cor............ co_me dian _zi par_
Tell me a - gain that our love is for-
MOLTO MENO
p
allarg.
CAV.
_la - vi, è co _ sì dol_ce il suon del _ la tua
ev- er. It is so sweet to hear you make that
col canto
f
p
(With almost ecstatic abandon.)
a tempo, ma sostenendo
T.
U_niti ed esu_lanti diffonde_rem pel mondo i nostri a_
U- nit- ed and en-chant-ed, guard-ing the flame that now is on- ly
CAV.
vo - ce!
prom ise.
28
a tempo, ma sostenuto
pp
cres. a poco a poco

cres ........................ e
T.
_mo _ ri armo_nie di co_lo _ ri, armo_ni _ e di
em- ber, our_ love will re- mem- ber that the hope we cre-
(In exaltation.)
CAV.
Armo_ni _ e di
that the hope we cre-
allarg. molto
T
can _ ti dif _ fon _ de _ rem....
a- ted nev- er can die!
CAV.
can _ ti dif _ fon _ de _ rem....
a- ted nev- er can die!
cres. e allarg. molto
f
secca

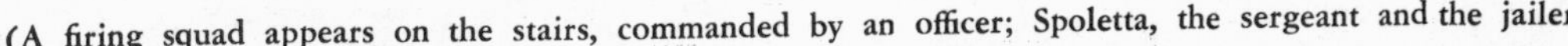
(A firing squad appears on the stairs, commanded by an officer; Spoletta, the sergeant and the jailer

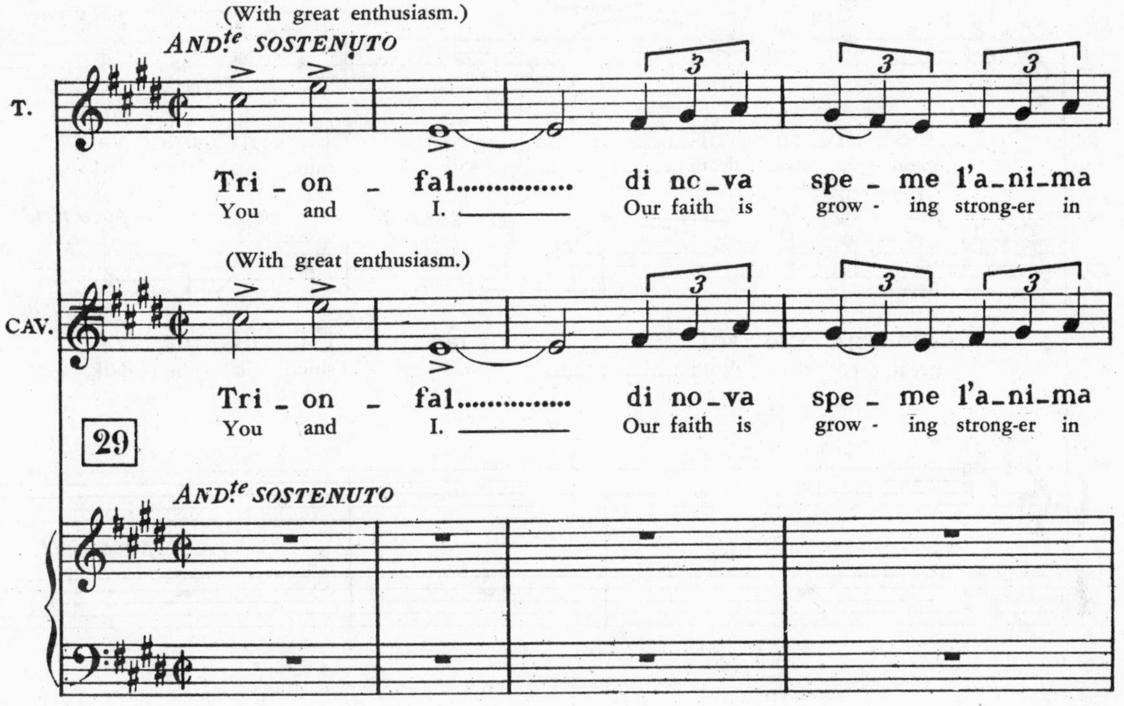


follow. Spoletta gives instructions.)

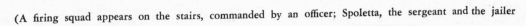

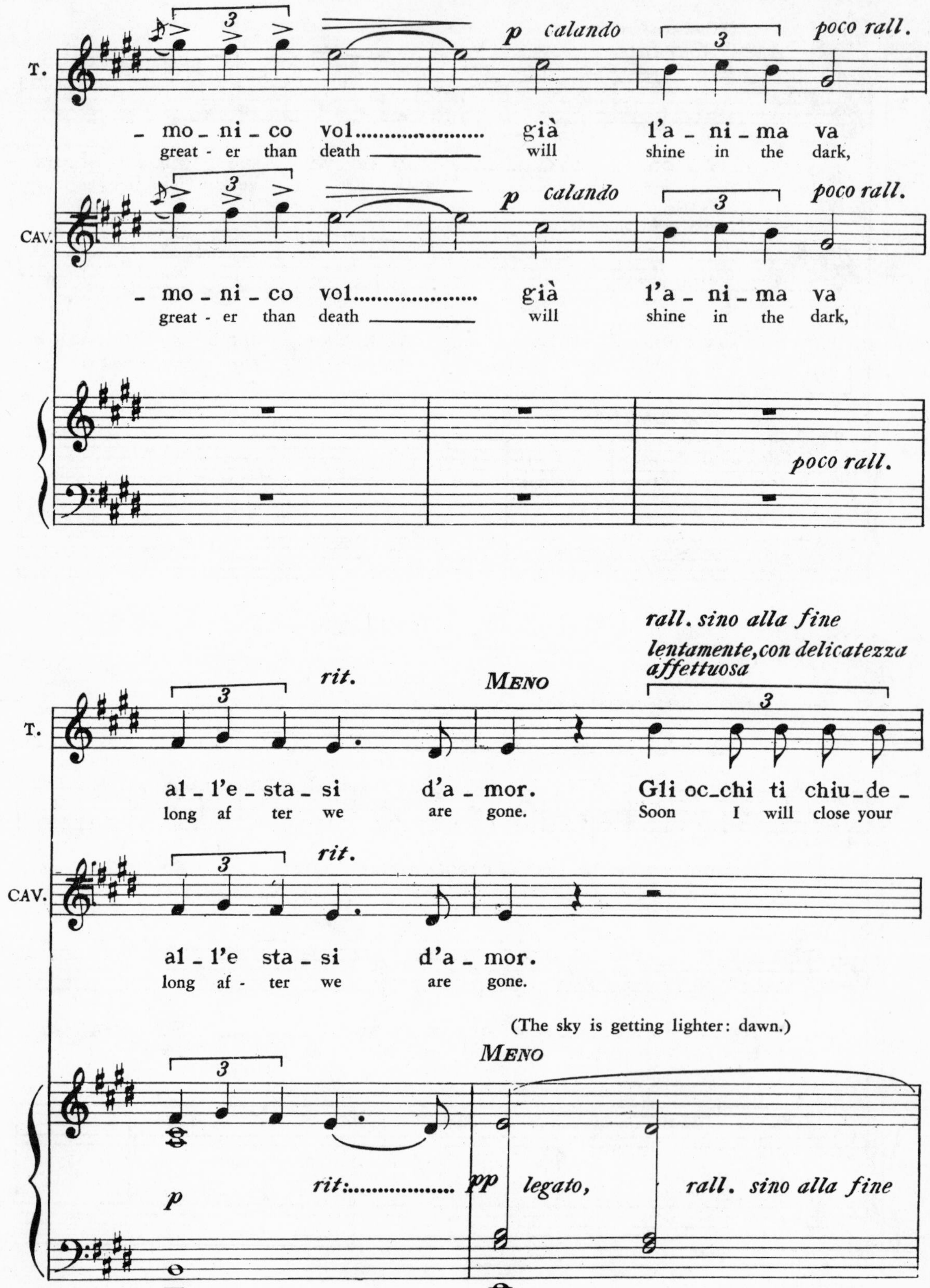

rall. sino alla fine
lentamente, con delicatezza affettuosa

rit. MENO

T.
al _ l'e _ sta _ si d'a _ mor. Gli oc_chi ti chiu_de _
long af ter we are gone. Soon I will close your

rit.

CAV.
al _ l'e sta _ si d'a _ mor.
long af - ter we are gone.

(The sky is getting lighter: dawn.)

MENO

p rit:.................. pp legato, rall. sino alla fine

rit.
pp rall.
T.
_rò con mil_le ba_ci e mil_le ti di_rò nomi d'a_
eyes with ten- der kiss - es, and whis- per words of love in - to your
rit.
pp rall:......
_mor..........................
ear.
CAVAR.
Son
I'm
(Walking up to Cavaradossi he takes off his cap, points to the officer; with the register under his arm, he descends the stairs.)
CARC.
L'o_ra!
Read- y?
Campana
(The clock strikes four.)
30
......ppp
molto
col canto........

(To Cavaradossi, under her breath, and almost laughing.)
AND.no SOSTENUTO
pp
T.
(Tie_ni a men _ te:... al
Now re - mem - ber — you
CAV.
pron _ to.
read - y.
AND.no SOSTENUTO
pp
ppp
primo colpo,... giù...)
hear a vol- ley: Fall!
(In a low voice, also laughing.)
pp
(Giù).
Yes.
(Nè rial_
Do not
_zar_ti in_nanzi ch'io ti chia_mi).
make an- y move un- til I call you!
(No, a _ mo _ re!)
No, my dar- ling.
(E ca_di
Be care - ful
sempre pp

(Seeing him smile.)

T.: be - ne.) (Non
fal - ling. No

(Smiling.)

CAV.: (Co - me la To - sca in te - a - tro.)
Like Flo - ria To - sca, the ac - tress?

T.: ridere...) (Co - sì).
laughing now! Like this.

(Seriously.)

CAV.: (Cò - sì?)
Like this?

rall.

31

rall.

(Cavaradossi, having said farewell to Tosca, follows the officer; Tosca remains in the cell. She is in a position that allows her to see what is happening on the platform.)

LARGO CON GRAVITÀ ♩=52

*p*

*espressivo*

*p*

*pp*

(She sees the officer and the sergeant who lead Cavaradossi to the opposite wall. The sergeant

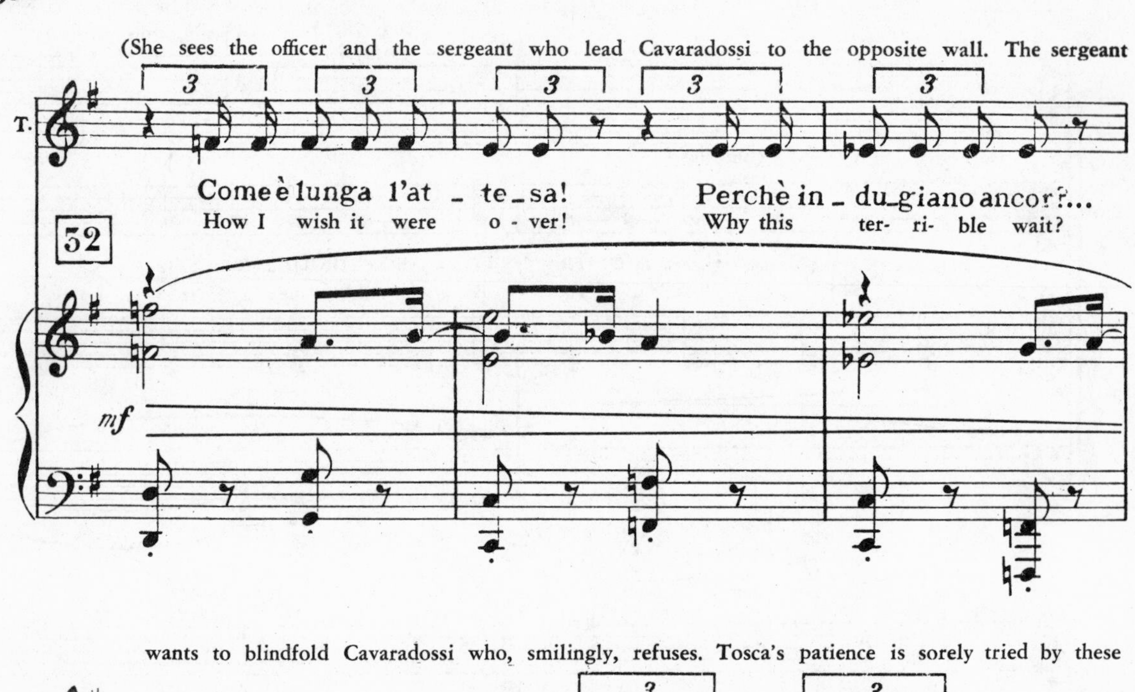
T.
3
Come è lunga l'at - te-sa! Perchè in - du-giano ancor?...
How I wish it were o - ver! Why this ter- ri- ble wait?
32
mf

wants to blindfold Cavaradossi who, smilingly, refuses. Tosca's patience is sorely tried by these

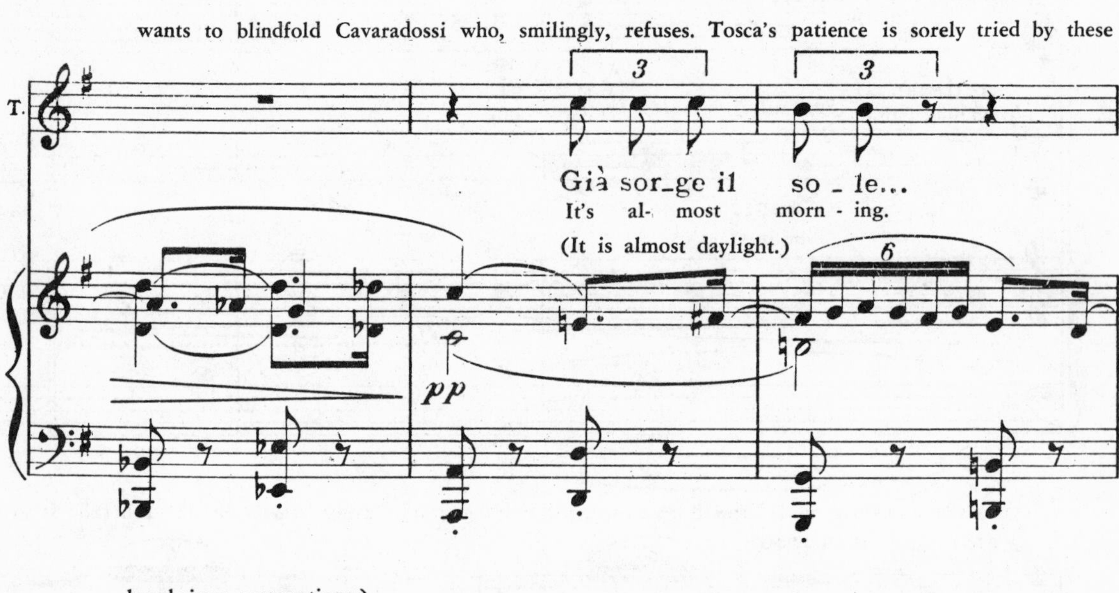
T.
3
Già sor-ge il so - le...
It's al- most morn - ing.
(It is almost daylight.)
6
pp

lugubrious preparations.)

T.
3
Per-chè in - du - gia - no an - co - ra?...
What on earth do they wait for?
6

33
è u_na commedia,
It's on- ly act- ing,
lo so....
I know,
mf
ma que_sta an_go_scia e_ter_na
and yet this wait- ing makes me
pa_re!...
trem- ble.
(The officer and the sergeant
p
order the soldiers to take up their positions.)
sostenendo il tempo
Ec_co!... appre_sta_no
There now — it seems they are
cres: . . . . .e. . . .sostenendo il tempo

T.
l'ar_mi...
ready.
34
f m.s.
m.d.
m.s.
ff
(Seeing the officer about to lower his sabre, Tosca raises her hands to her ears so as not to hear the
quasi parlato
6
come è bello il mio
He is hand-some, my
(The officer lowers
cres. ancora
stentato
fff
shots; she beckons to Cavaradossi to fall down, saying:)
(Seeing Cavaradossi on the ground, she throws him a kiss with her hand.)
Ma_rio!.. Là! muo_ri! Ec_co un ar-
Ma- rio! There! Fall now! He's such an
his sabre.)
(The shots ring out.)
35
cres.
fff (subito dopo la parola della battuta successiva)

(The sergeant approaches Cavaradossi and scrutinizes his body: Spoletta stops the sergeant from giving Cavaradossi the coup de grace. The officer orders the soldiers to fall in line again; the sergeant relieves the rear sentry; all, preceded by Spoletta, walk down the stairs.)

Iº TEMPO
T.
_ti _ sta!...
art- ist.
ff Iº TEMPO
(Tosca, in great agitation, has closely watched all these moves, fearing that Cavaradossi, getting impatient, might move or get up too early.)
fff marcatissimo
dim.
TOSCA
con voce repressa quasi parlato
pp
O Ma_rio, non ti muove_re... s'avvi_a_no...
Be care-ful, do not move too soon. They're leav-ing now —
p
T.
ta_ci! vanno.... scendo_no....
qui- et. They are — leav-ing now,
36
pp

(Suspecting that the soldiers might yet return, she again addresses Cavaradossi.)
T.
scendo no. _
leav-ing now.
Anco _ ra non ti muovere...
One mo ment, do not move too soon.
ppp
(Tosca rushes to the parapet and, leaning over, looks down.)
T.
dim.
perdendosi
(Going closer to Cavaradossi.)
A PIACERE - MOSSO
p (Almost spoken.)
T.
Pre _ sto, su!
Now they're gone.
Mario!
Ma- rio,
Mario!
Ma-rio.
Su,
Get
col canto

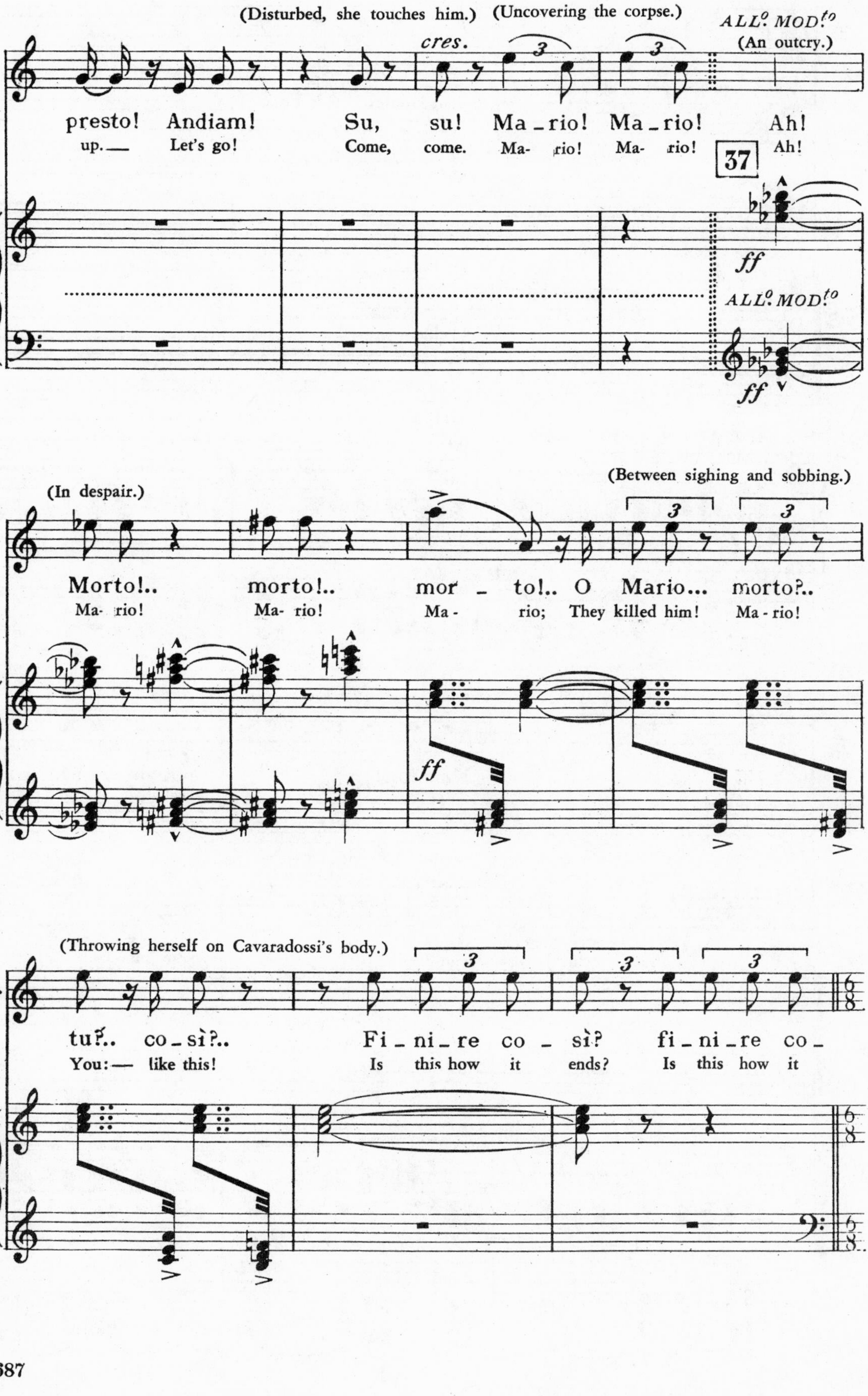

(Disturbed, she touches him.) (Uncovering the corpse.) ALL.º MOD.to

(An outcry.)

T.

cres.

presto! Andiam! Su, su! Ma_rio! Ma_rio! Ah!

up.— Let's go! Come, come. Ma- rio! Ma- rio! Ah!

37

ff

ALL.º MOD.to

ff

(In despair.) (Between sighing and sobbing.)

T.

Morto!.. morto!.. mor _ to!.. O Mario... morto?..

Ma- rio! Ma- rio! Ma - rio; They killed him! Ma - rio!

ff

AGITATO ♩.= 116
(Embracing Cavaradossi's lifeless form.)
T
SPOL. - sì!
ends?
(From downstairs.)
Tu, mor_to... morto?
Dead — Ma-rio, Ma-rio!
(Prolonged cries from a distance.)
Ah! Ah!
SCIARR.
Ah! Ah!
Tenori
Ah! Ah!
Bassi
ALCUNI SOLDATI
Ah! Ah!
AGITATO ♩.= 116
38
pp
(Crying.)
string. a poco a poco
T.
Ma_rio... po_ve_ra Flo_ria
Ma-rio! (Yelling.) What shall I do with-
SPOL.
f Scarpia? Ah!
Scar- pia? Ah!
SCI.
Vi di_co, pugna_la_to!
I tell you: he was mur-dered!
Scarpia.
Scar- pia.
f Scarpia? Ah!
Scar- pia? Ah!
f Scarpia? Ah!
Scar- pia? Ah!
p string. a poco a poco e cres.

T.
tu - a!
out you?
Ma - rio!
Ma- rio!
Ma - rio!
Ma- rio!
SPOL
La donna è Tosca!
Mur-dered by To-sca!
SCI.
Che non sfug-ga!
We must catch her.
Che non sfug-ga!
We must catch her.
Che non sfug-ga!
We must catch her.
(Weeping desperately, she throws herself on Cavaradossi's corpse.)
(Coming closer.)
(Close-by.)
Atten-ti agli sbocchi delle scale!
At once, post a guard at eve-ry ex-it.
Atten-ti agli sbocchi delle scale!
At once, post a guard at eve-ry ex-it.
Atten-ti agli sbocchi delle scale!
At once, post a guard at eve-ry ex-it.
Atten-ti agli sbocchi delle scale!
At once, post a guard at eve-ry ex-it.
Atten-ti agli sbocchi delle scale!
At once, post a guard at eve-ry ex-it.
Atten-ti agli sbocchi delle scale!
At once, post a guard at eve-ry ex-it.
mf cres.

(A great noise is heard from downstairs.)
39
p
cres. e string. molto
(Spoletta and Sciarrone appear at the top of the stairs.)
f
SPOL.
(Pointing to Tosca, he cries.)
Ah!
Ah,
To - - sca,
To-
sca!
SCIARR.
40
È
She's
lei!
here!
ff

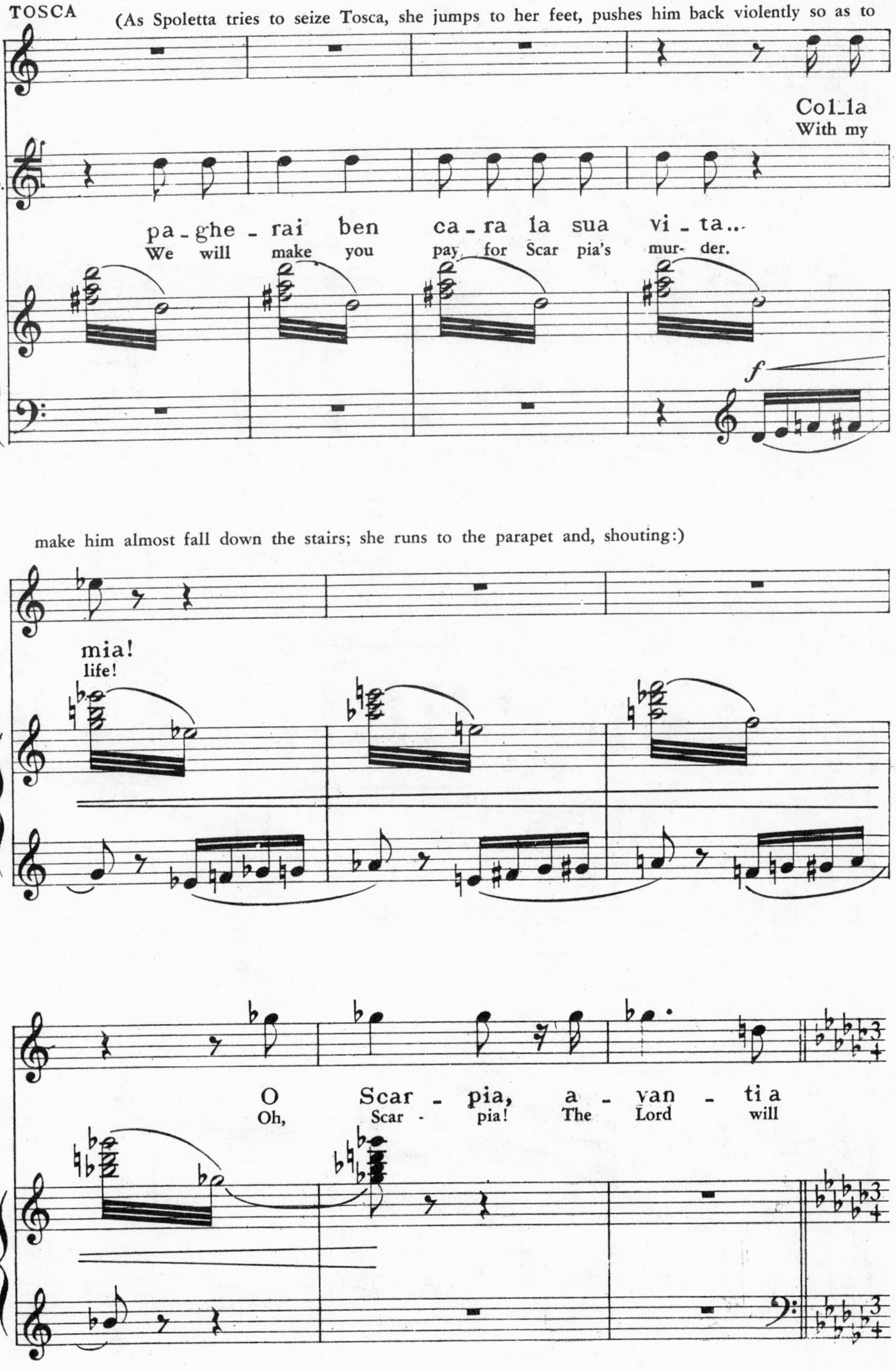

make him almost fall down the stairs; she runs to the parapet and, shouting:)

T.

mia!
life!

T.

O Scar - pia, a - van - ti a
Oh, Scar - pia! The Lord will

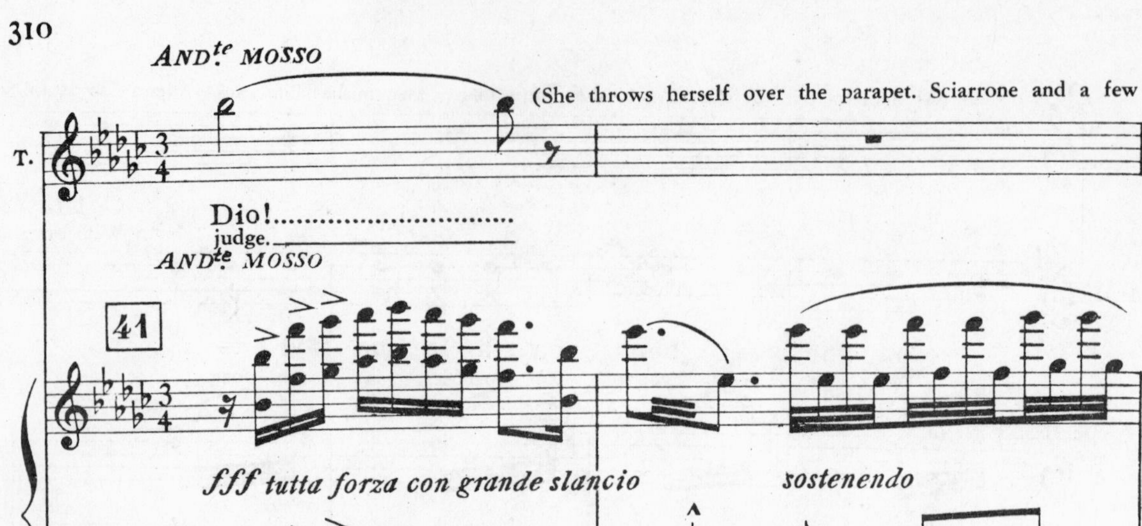

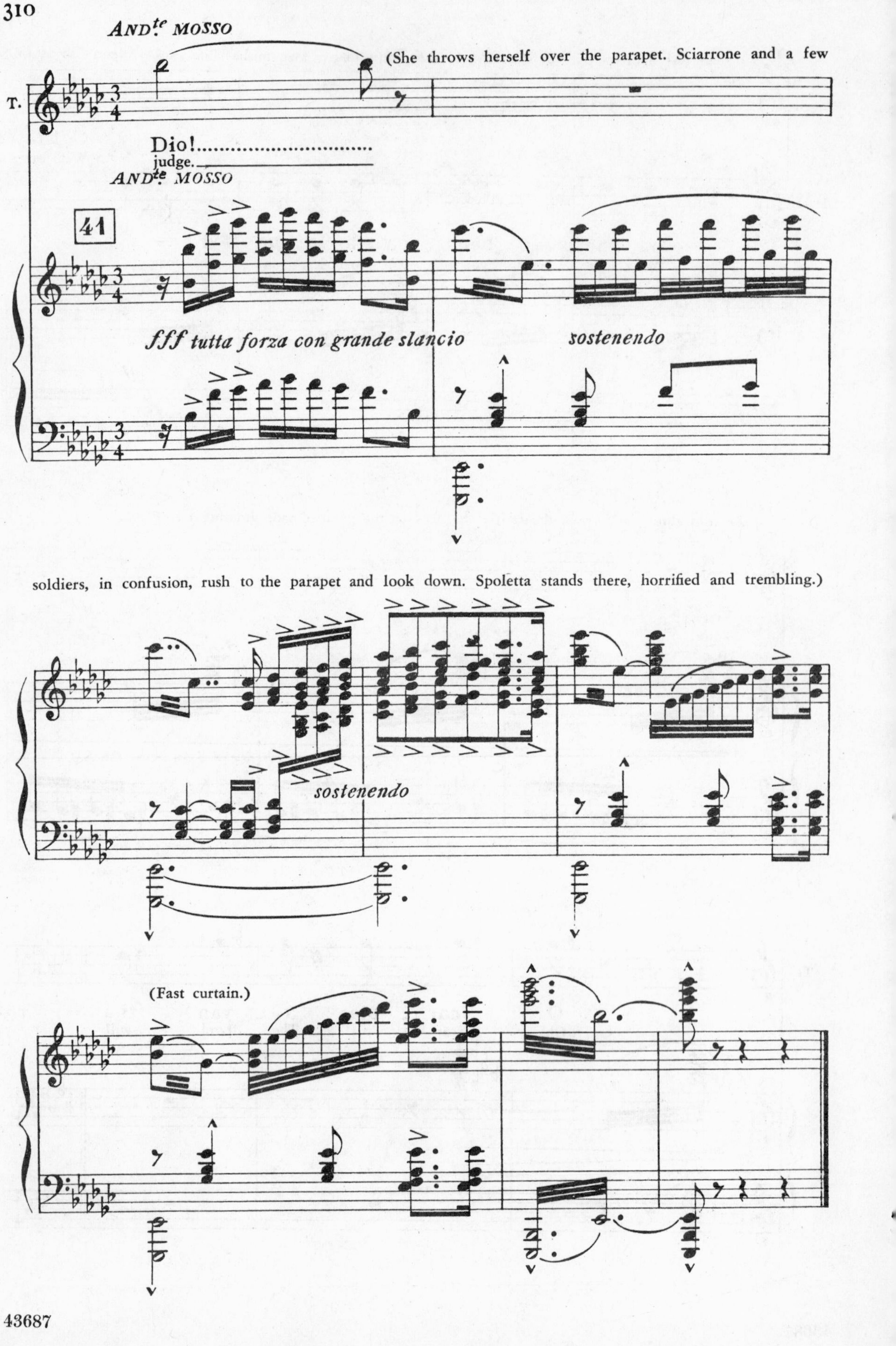

ANDte MOSSO
(She throws herself over the parapet. Sciarrone and a few
T.
Dio!
judge.
ANDte MOSSO
41
fff tutta forza con grande slancio
sostenendo
soldiers, in confusion, rush to the parapet and look down. Spoletta stands there, horrified and trembling.)
sostenendo
(Fast curtain.)